THE BBC PRESENTS THE 109TH SEASON
OF HENRY WOOD PROMENADE CONCERTS

BBC PROMS

18 JULY – 13 SEPTEMBER 2003

The Proms: a continuing history of innovation

Queen's Hall

Henry Wood

Royal Albert Hall

Leonard Slatkin

BBC Prom in the Park

The Proms were founded to bring the best of classical music to a wide audience in an informal setting. From the outset, part of the audience has always stood in the 'promenade'. Prom places originally cost just a shilling; today, standing places at the Royal Albert Hall still cost only £4.00, and over 1,000 tickets go on sale for every concert from an hour beforehand. Programmes have always mixed the great classics with what Henry Wood, first conductor of the Proms, called his 'novelties' – rare works and premieres. **1895** The 26-year-old Wood is chosen to launch the Promenade Concerts at the newly opened Queen's Hall; Wood conducts the Proms throughout their first 50 years. **1927** The BBC takes over the running of the Proms. **1930** The new BBC Symphony Orchestra becomes the orchestra of the Proms; the BBC's own orchestras still provide the backbone of the season. **1941** The Proms move to the Royal Albert Hall after the Queen's Hall is gutted in an air raid. **1942** The BBC SO shares the season with another orchestra for the first time. **1944** Henry Wood dies shortly after celebrating his Proms jubilee. **1947** First televised Last Night. **1950** Malcolm Sargent becomes Chief Conductor of the BBC SO. **1953** First out-of-London orchestra at the Proms. **1960** First Proms commission. **1961** First complete opera at the Proms: Mozart's *Don Giovanni*, from the Glyndebourne Festival. **1966** First foreign orchestra at the Proms. **1968** First Friday-night First Night. **1970** First Late Night Prom: cult pop group The Soft Machine. **1971** First 'world music' Prom: sitar-player Imrat Khan. **1974** First Pre-Prom Talks. **1994** The Proms' 100th season features a retrospective of past premieres. **1995** The Proms' centenary season features a record number of new commissions. **1996** First Prom in the Park, first Proms Chamber Music series and first Proms Lecture. **1997** First Proms solo recital: pianist Evgeny Kissin. **1998** First Blue Peter Family Prom. **2000** First Poetry Proms. **2001** Leonard Slatkin becomes Chief Conductor of the BBC SO. **2002** The Proms go digital on BBC4. **2003** The Proms go fully interactive on digital satellite and freeview TV.

The BBC: bringing the Proms to you, wherever you are – on radio, television and the internet

www.bbc.co.uk/proms

Your Guide to the Proms 2003

Welcome to the BBC Proms 2003: the very best of great music, available to all. The *BBC Proms Guide 2003* provides all you need to plan your concert-going, listening or viewing, and to book your tickets quickly and easily.

Season Theme pages 4–23

Ancient Greek myths have resonated across the centuries, stimulating great art in all forms. Berlioz's epic opera *The Trojans* under Sir Colin Davis is the centrepiece of a season that features other mythological operas, including Richard Strauss's *Elektra*, Purcell's *Dido and Aeneas* and Tippett's *King Priam*, as well as more myth-inspired works by Stravinsky, Britten, Mendelssohn and Nielsen, and living composers from Birtwistle to Woolrich.

Anniversary Composers pages 30–45

Our Berlioz bicentenary celebration includes his thrilling early opera *Benvenuto Cellini* and his lyrical oratorio *The Childhood of Christ*. We also mark the 50th anniversary of Prokofiev's death with his film score for *Ivan the Terrible* conducted by Leonard Slatkin, his opera *War and Peace* from English National Opera, and some important rarities. A huge Baroque orchestra is specially convened for Corelli's 350th birthday, while we acknowledge the anniversaries of many other major composers from Arnold Bax and Lennox Berkeley to Thea Musgrave and György Ligeti.

Season Highlights pages 52–57

The Proms reach 'wider still and wider' with the Late 'Late Junction' Prom, a wide-ranging musical marathon inspired by Radio 3's eclectic cult programme. Glyndebourne Festival Opera brings *Die Fledermaus*, Dame Felicity Lott sings Poulenc's one-woman *tour de force*, *La voix humaine*, Paul McCreesh directs Handel's *Saul* and Sakari Oramo conducts Tchaikovsky's rarely heard *Manfred* symphony.

New Music pages 66–75

We bring you the finest new scores by composers from around the world. Adams, Birtwistle, Goebbels, Gruber, Knussen, Pintscher, Weir: their best recent work is showcased alongside commissions from many British composers – including a work from Joseph Phibbs for the Last Night – making the Proms an unrivalled patron of the best in new music.

Proms Artists pages 82–88

Alongside the BBC's outstanding orchestras and choirs, we welcome the new partnership of Sir Simon Rattle and the Berliner Philharmoniker, a return visit by Mariss Jansons and the Pittsburgh Symphony, the Vienna Philharmonic teamed with the unique singer-conductor Bobby McFerrin, and Daniel Barenboim with his inspiring West-Eastern Divan youth orchestra.

Proms Extras pages 129–136

The Proms reach out to new audiences: John Adams and the BBC Symphony Orchestra play to young people at the Brixton Academy. Controversial director Peter Sellars gives the BBC Proms Lecture on the potent relevance of Greek myths to us today. Proms Composer Portraits and Proms Chamber Music recitals take place at the Victoria & Albert Museum. And, on the season's final weekend, Proms in the Park reaches all four nations of the UK for the first time.

Proms Broadcasts pages 140–143

A new 'Nation's Favourite Prom' includes Sir David Attenborough and a selection of arias for you, the audience, to choose. A fortnight of Proms on BBC4 and a rich selection on BBC1 and BBC2 include new interactive features, and every concert is broadcast live on BBC Radio 3 and online.

Booking Information pages 89–128

Complete concert listings, ticket offers (including special 'Odyssey' and weekend passes), and our easy-to-fax priority booking form are included in the central booking section of this *Guide*. Enjoy the season!

Nicholas Kenyon

Nicholas Kenyon
Director, BBC Proms

GREEK MYTHS

Singing to generations yet to come

The myths of ancient Greece can still speak to us after almost 3,000 years. Neil MacGregor, **director of the British Museum, suggests some reasons why**

ABOVE
Homer, the singer of tales: an imaginary marble portrait bust (2nd century AD Roman copy of a Hellenistic original), on show at the British Museum

RIGHT
The first meeting of Helen and Paris, with Aphrodite and Eros looking on: a red-figure vase (Campanian, 4th century BC), on show at the British Museum

In the sixth book of Homer's *Iliad* captive Helen muses on the many sufferings of war that her presence in Troy and her love for Paris have inflicted upon the Trojans. She complains that Zeus, king of the gods, has imposed an evil fate upon them all, 'so that we might be sung about by generations yet to come'.

Helen's prediction was resoundingly fulfilled. Yet not even she, vain and self-absorbed as she was, could possibly have guessed at just how different European civilisation – not to mention the contents of this year's Proms season or London's museums and art galleries – would have been had her elopement not precipitated so many and such complex catastrophes for both Greeks and Trojans, including almost every member of her and Paris's extended families. Future generations – Shakespeare and Goethe, Freud and Purcell, Berlioz and Turner, Rubens, Racine, Gluck, Titian, Tippett, Joyce and the Coen Brothers – would indeed sing and psychoanalyse, paint, write and film the endless consequences of Helen walking out on her husband. Her domestic drama has shaped our world.

For a moment let us conjure an ideal, century-spanning panel of cultural heavyweights, miraculously convoked for a special Proms interval feature on TV.

The subject for discussion: the dysfunctional life of Helen's nephew and nieces – Orestes, Iphigenia and Electra. Depending on whether this is to be broadcast on BBC1 or BBC2, Offenbach or Gluck will be in the chair, to get proceedings off to an appropriately flip or solemn start. Racine explains to us why a family is bound to fall apart when the father sacrifices his children to wider ambitions; Freud speculates on how a son resolves the guilt of killing his mother; Strauss focuses on the frustrations of a daughter left at home who feels defiled by her mother's infidelities; and Goethe's Iphigenia, like the great German himself, looks to the gods to vindicate her own moral convictions. All four panellists

succeed in making the characters and their situations disconcertingly actual for us, the audience. Their dilemmas, we are made to believe, are essentially ours. And the purpose of the artist is not so much an Aristotelian purging of our emotions, as to lead us through empathy to understanding.

I think it is fair to say that the Greeks would probably not have seen it in such overwhelmingly human terms. But these are no longer the myths of the Greeks. By now, they are ours, and we have made them into the myths *we* need, the stories through which we seek to understand ourselves. Only the stories of the Bible have offered food so rich to the European tradition.

In Homer's evocative passage on Helen's dawning understanding of the scale of her disaster, we already perceive one of the *Iliad*'s defining characteristics: that groping awareness which Homer grants to his characters of their roles as players in a drama essentially shaped by forces outside their control, but none the less partly of their own making. If the gods can be cruel, humans also construct their own destiny by ill-judged words and misconceived actions. We are co-authors of our fate. There is no ultimate salvation on offer here from a providential deity, no assurances of future happiness or of triumphant justice (no threats of Armagedd Ragnarök either). There is r loss, conflict and misun course, there are als

9

recognition and realisation, the more remarkable because they are achieved on the human level, not through divine intervention. They are perhaps all that can be achieved by humans. And though they lead only to an acknowledgement of the bitterness of the human predicament, rather than to any kind of solution, that in itself offers some kind of dignity in the face of doom. It is surely the power of this tragic insight that has made the Greek myths such a compelling and inexhaustible resource for dramatists, artists and musicians.

In this alien world, divine power is great, but not absolute. It is often at odds with itself, it can be arbitrary and it is not always benign. We are very far from the familiar benevolence of the one Jewish, Christian or Muslim God, even further from a scientifically ordered universe. And the relationship between gods and humans is to us equally strange. The Greek gods were not mankind's creators, but they could be its immediate progenitors – many Greeks of noble birth claimed divine descent. Where Judaism, Islam and Christianity set a great gulf between the human and the divine (hence the endless disputes around the Incarnation), Greek paganism sees a continuous spectrum. The Gods are like us, even if we can only intermittently be like them. They play with us and punish us. Wanton gods indeed.

Does it matter (it is often said to) that this world-view is today irrecoverably remote and the stories unknown? I think not, for a great myth will always get through, even a complex one. Almost ~ry day in the National Gallery you

can see groups of children sitting in front of Titian's *Bacchus and Ariadne*. For Christian neo-Platonists of the Renaissance this was a rich and recondite tale: Bacchus the wine-god, prefiguring the Eucharist, with Ariadne the despairing soul, pursued by divine love. Or, if you wanted to stay in the pre-Christian classical tradition, you could quibble over the transformation of a Cretan story by those Roman poets Ovid and Catullus.

We can, I think, assume that the seven-year-olds in Trafalgar Square know little of this. Yet the ultramarine sky can be read by them all as speaking not of London but of a dream-world of perpetual holiday. They may not know if it is Mediterranean or Caribbean sky (Derek Walcott would not care) and it doesn't matter. It takes but gentle question-and-answering for them to get to the essentials: a lonely lady is about to have something very nice happen to her. Sadness will be overwhelmed in joy, if the unhappy person allows it, and the joy will be human, animal and divine, all at once. A party is at hand. Happiness has won.

The myth has done its work, perhaps the more powerfully because the protagonists are now meaningless other than as archetypes – Ariadne is simply a person waiting for happiness, like lots of people we know, like ourselves. And this is surely one of the huge advantages enjoyed today by stories from pagan religions long safely dead. They have no sect to claim

ABOVE
'A beauty contest nobody would now dare organise': *The Judgement of Paris* by Peter Paul Rubens (1577–1640), on show at the National Gallery

BELOW LEFT
X-rated viewing: a portrait of Medusa, the snake-haired Gorgon, painted on a leather jousting shield by Caravaggio (c1571–1610)

them. If narratives from the Bible (or from other holy scriptures) may easily be set aside as meaningless by those who do not believe, these pagan myths have value for all, because they can now be read only as universal. A few yards from *Bacchus and Ariadne* hangs another painting by Titian made at roughly the same time and also showing an affectionate god offering consolation and hope to a distraught woman: it is the risen Christ appearing to Mary Magdalen. Yet how many visitors to the National Gallery can use it to explore their own experience in the way they can use the *Bacchus and Ariadne*?

The world of Greek myth is not just a storehouse of incomparable narrative power. It is a visual gold mine. Battles between dragon-slaying heroes and fantastic monsters have always played to huge crowds, with Hercules and Perseus on one side, Cerberus the three-headed hell-hound and Medusa, the snake-haired Gorgon, on the other. They kept Titian and Caravaggio in subject-matter that thrilled and

RIGHT
'A lonely lady is about to have something very nice happen to her': *Bacchus and Ariadne* by Titian (c1485–1576), on show at the National Gallery

sold. You need no knowledge to understand this. You just enjoy. It is a wonderfully permissive tradition for a civilisation structured and strictured by St Paul. No wonder Renaissance Europe leapt at it, for classical myth still offers licensed violence and dangerous sex at levels that can shock. In the National Gallery, Rubens's three goddesses shamelessly undress for two very intent male watchers, in a beauty contest nobody would now dare organise. And in Cornelis van Haarlem's spasm of blood-lust, Cadmus' followers are torn limb from limb, with a severed and partly chewed head prominent in the foreground. Parents complain that it should not be hung where children can see it, and it would certainly not be shown on television before the 9 o'clock watershed. If you want to walk on the dark side, it is all here for you.

For a more cerebral, gentler public, Claude and Poussin could evoke a different Greek world-view, filtered and sweetened by Ovid's *Metamorphoses*. Not much gore to unsettle you here, but a mild disapproval of excessive desire, which the gods punish with apposite – sometimes sternly apposite – humour. At the worst you might be turned into a spring flower, a crow or a heifer, and that probably in a sunny landscape, leaving you to ponder, in a wistful 17th-century way, the essential one-ness of the created world.

We humans are not often like the gods, these myths tell us, and we know that to be true. But are we at least like each other? We hope so and sometimes the texts support us. The *Iliad* is

it is on the surviving pots, deformed the refined and politically sophisticated rulers of Persepolis into bestial tyrants, dominated by pleasure and vice, deserving only of contempt from the austere, rational Greeks. And it can be no coincidence that the struggle shown on the Parthenon metopes now in the British Museum is not between men and men, but between the civilised human Lapiths and the half-bestial Centaurs. In this monument to the self-image of Athens after its victory over Persia, a new – very much post-Trojan – myth is on view. The foreigner is now irredeemably other, the enemy has become less than human.

Tragically, it is perhaps this later Greek myth that we have in the last hundred years made most fully our own. Like the Greeks after the Persian wars, we have lost the concept of the honourable foe. All our enemies are now centaurs. Helen would not have understood.

ABOVE AND LEFT
In Homer, Greeks and Trojans share a common humanity, as shown (above) in a 5th-century BC red-figure vase-painting of Priam coming to Achilles' tent to beg for his dead son's body. Contrast the scene (left) from the Battle of the Lapiths and Centaurs, one of the Parthenon metopes, in which, after the Persian wars, 'the enemy has become less than human'. Both works are on show at the British Museum

ABOVE
'A shrewdly beguiling Southern country bumpkin': George Clooney as escaped convict Ulysses Everett McGill in the Coen Brothers' 2000 film O Brother, Where Art Thou?, loosely based on Homer's Odyssey

eloquent of the essential sameness of the opposing peoples. Greeks and Trojans play the game of war by the same rules, or at least break them in the same way. Each understands the grief of the other. Hector taking leave of his wife and son is every man going off to war. When Priam and Achilles meet and the father pleads for his dead son's body, there is no sense at all that Trojans feel either less than, or differently from, the Greek warriors on the other side or – more startling still – from the Greeks at home listening to the story being sung.

The desire to find our common humanity shapes the way we interpret the tales. We want to be able to understand,

even to sympathise with Medea, to see her above all as a wife abandoned by a glib and opportunistic husband and left with the children, and we are thrown and irritated that she is also of divine descent. When we rewrite the stories ourselves, the heroes become even more like the people we know: Joyce's Ulysses a workaday Dublin businessman, the Coen Brothers' Ulysses a shrewdly beguiling Southern country bumpkin.

But the common humanity of the *Iliad* that so touches us did not survive the Greek wars against the Persians in the 5th century BC. A propaganda campaign of moral denigration of the defeated enemy, legible in Aeschylus as

For 'Proms Extra' events at the British Museum and National Gallery, see pages 134–5

LEFT
The 'Achilles' statue in Hyde Park: cast from cannon captured in the Peninsular War, erected in 1822 as a monument to the Duke of Wellington and paid for by 'the ladies of England' (many of whom were outraged by its nudity), the statue is in fact modelled on one of the two 'horse-tamers' on the Quirinale in Rome (themselves Roman copies of 5th-century BC Greek originals)

FESTIVAL 2003

Challenging, moving, entertaining, profound...

illuminating

FIRST WEEK 10 - 16 AUGUST

Complete Ring Cycle, *Glagolitic Mass*, Petra Lang, *Lohengrin*, Los Angeles Philharmonic Orchestra, Hillevi Martinpelto, *The Seagull*, John Relyea, Pansori, Cullberg Ballet, Ian Bostridge, Periferico de Objectos, Donald Runnicles, the music of Guo Wenjing, Nitin Sawhney and Takemitsu

SECOND WEEK 17 - 23 AUGUST

Bernard Haitink, *Amadigi*, Emmanuelle Haïm, Alfred Brendel, Bordeaux Opera Ballet, Leonidas Kavakos, Sir Charles Mackerras, Alice Coote, Ingo Metzmacher, *Hamlet*, Steven Osborne, *Picasso and Dance*, Rinaldo Alessandrini, Calixto Bieito, András Schiff, the complete Beethoven string quartets

THIRD WEEK 24 - 30 AUGUST

Violeta Urmana, San Francisco Ballet, complete Ring Cycle, Hélène Grimaud, *Macbeth*, Bamberg Symphony Orchestra, Jonathan Nott, *Strictly Dandia*, Sir Charles Mackerras, Murray Perahia, Thomas Trotter, Lausanne Chamber Orchestra, *Zelmira*, Thomas Quasthoff, the complete string quartets of Elliott Carter

Edinburgh
International FESTIVAL

BOOK NOW   0131 473 2000   www.eif.co.uk

10 - 30 August

PUEBLO DoN THOMAS
a New World brought closer to you

LA GOMERA · CANARY ISLANDS

EXCLUSIVE RESIDENTIAL COMPLEX · APARTMENTS · VILLAS · TECINA GOLF · PUEBLO DON THOMAS
Tel: (+34) 922.628.380 www.pueblodonthomas.com

FRED. OLSEN, S.A.

for information about OUP
composers please contact:
Repertoire Promotion Department
70 Baker Street, London W1U 7DN
tel: +44 (0)20 7616 5900
fax: +44 (0)20 7616 5901

OXFORD

gerald barry • michael berkeley • benjamin britten • john buller • martin butler • andrew carter • richard causton • www.oup.com/uk/music • bob chilcott • gordon crosse • gabriel erkoreka • michael finnissy • john gardner • roberto gerhard • edward harper • alun hoddinott • constant lambert • libby larsen • zhou long • william mathias • gerald plain • alan rawsthorne • john rutter • robert sherlaw johnson • howard skempton • hilary tann • phyllis tate • michael thomas • ralph vaughan williams • william walton • zhou long • grace williams • gerald barry • michael berkeley • benjamin britten • john buller • martin butler • repertoire.promotion@oup.co.uk • richard causton • bob chilcott • gordon crosse • gabriel erkoreka • michael finnissy • john gardner • roberto gerhard • edward harper • alun hoddinott • constant lambert • libby larsen • william mathias • gerald plain • anthony powers • andrew carter •

exciting music worldwide...

Remaking myths in music

From the earliest operas to the latest Proms commissions, the Greek myths have fascinated composers, as Roderic Dunnett **reveals**

ABOVE
Iannis Xenakis: a 1984 portrait of the Greek composer whose *Idmen A & B* evokes a picture of the creation of the world using jumbled syllables from Hesiod's *Theogony*

ABOVE
Imaginary likeness of Hesiod, the early Greek poet (*c*700 BC) whose *Theogony* is the source for many Greek myths: Roman marble copy of a 2nd century BC Hellenistic original, on show at the British Museum

RIGHT
Saturn Devouring One of His Own Children (1823) by Goya

Music often figures in Greek mythology – be it the story of Pan carving the first pan-pipes from a reed, Apollo flaying poor Marsyas alive for daring to beat him in a talent contest, or Orpheus charming Death itself with his song. And Greek myths have played a decisive role in music, opera especially.

It was Nietzsche who first wrote of the 'Birth of Tragedy from the Spirit of Music', tracing the primacy of the chorus in engendering the earliest Greek dramas. In using Greek tragedy and its mythical content to inspire a brand-new art form, the earliest opera composers – musicians at the Renaissance court of the Medici in Florence – repaid the compliment.

The first known 'musical drama' was Jacopo Peri's myth-based *Dafne*, premiered at the Florentine carnival of 1598. It was closely followed by two rival versions of *Euridice*. So the legend of Orpheus, the very personification of Greek music, was in at the very start of this new genre, a genre that aspired, like Greek tragedy itself, to knit many art forms – music, dance, drama, poetry, song, design – into one.

And it was the Orpheus myth once more that inspired what is unarguably the first great opera, and the earliest to survive in the repertoire – Monteverdi's *L'Orfeo* – premiered in 1607 in Mantua, birthplace of the Roman poet

Virgil, whose farming manual *The Georgics* coincidentally offers the *locus classicus* for the Orpheus legend.

Countless composers ever since have ransacked the Greek myths for inspiration. Like Greek tragedy, most of the operas these myths inspired trace the uneasy dealings between men and gods, and highlight the fixed moral order that defines, constrains and underpins the universe. Thus Sophocles' *Electra* and *Antigone* – set to music by Richard Strauss and Felix Mendelssohn respectively – feature classic debates on

IN THE BEGINNING ...

Iannis Xenakis (1922–2001)

Idmen A & B
PROM 67

Born in Romania, the Greek composer Iannis Xenakis spent most of his life in exile in France after being sentenced to death in Greece for his part in the wartime resistance. A one-time assistant to the avant-garde architect Le Corbusier, he drew inspiration equally from non-western traditions and the literary and linguistic legacy of his ancient Greek ancestors.

Written in 1985, *Idmen A & B* harks back – like Holst's evocation of the earliest Greek deities, Uranus and his child-devouring son Saturn, in *The Planets* (Prom 60) – to a time in Greek mythology when the earth was in its infancy. With vigorous, jabbing music for percussion alternating with arresting choral passages – using jumbled syllables from the *Theogony* ('The Birth of the Gods') by the early Greek poet Hesiod – the two interlocking scores conjure up a vibrant picture of the world's emergence from primeval Chaos.

the rights and wrongs of independent action. When Strauss's *Electra* determines to avenge her dead father Agamemnon upon his murderer, her mother Clytemnestra, and savages her sister's cowardice for refusing to help, she lambasts inert apathy in us all.

Yet, though Freud coined the terms 'Oedipus Complex', to denote a boy's over-strong attachment to his mother, and 'Electra Complex', for a girl's to her father, the Greeks saw our lives as ruled more by fate than psychosis.

Doomed at birth by Apollo's oracle to murder his father and marry his mother, Oedipus' very survival in infancy subverts the moral order. His choices thereafter are blinded by what he (unlike the blind seer Tiresias) cannot know. By contrast, when, in Tippett's

IN THE HEAVENS ...

Carl Nielsen (1865–1931)
Helios
PROM 40

Thea Musgrave (born 1928)
Helios
PROM 51

Helios was the Greek Sun-god, who drove his flaming chariot, drawn by four fiery horses, daily across the sky, before returning, or so the Roman poet Ovid tells us, to his gold and ivory palace beyond the horizon. The Danish composer Carl Nielsen wrote his *Helios* overture in 1903 while on a visit to Greece, where he enjoyed brilliant sunlit views across the Aegean Sea. It is a work suffused with light and warmth, whose misty opening and magnificent tune, depicting a radiant sunrise, culminates in a triumphant fugue, before the sun unyokes his chariot and puts his horses quietly to bed.

The Scottish composer Thea Musgrave, who celebrates her 75th birthday this year, wrote her oboe concerto *Helios* for the St Magnus Festival, in Orkney, in 1994. Musgrave is among the most imaginative of orchestrators: this thrilling work begins serenely, but soon develops into a cloudy and stormy journey, with vivid writing for the solo oboe and graphic depiction (in wind and brass) of Helios's fiery steeds.

Igor Stravinsky (1882–1971)
Apollon musagète
PROM 5

Benjamin Britten (1913–76)
Young Apollo
PROM 51

Though often identified with Helios, Apollo was more than just another Sun-god. The deity of music and medicine, purification and prophecy, archers and athletes, Lord of Delphi and of the Nine Muses, he embodied all things Greek. Often depicted with a bow or lyre, his sacred emblems were the bay tree, the snake and (some said) the mouse. Stravinsky's ballet score *Apollon musagète* ('Apollo, leader of the Muses') is one of his most relaxed and charming works. Composed for strings alone, this 'Ballet to the Sun-god in the manner of *Le roi soleil*' draws inspiration from the French theatre of Louis XIV's time. Its 1928 Paris premiere marked Stravinsky's last collaboration with Serge Diaghilev, the impresario who had nurtured his career, and his first with George Balanchine, the choreographer with whom he was to work most closely thereafter.

Newly arrived in America in 1939, Britten was inspired by 'such sunshine as I've never seen before' to compose his 'bright and brilliant' piano-led fantasia *Young Apollo*, whose impetuous flair also derived from the final lines of Keats's unfinished poem *Hyperion* ('from all his limbs celestial'). Premiered in 1939, with Britten himself at the piano, it was not performed again for another 40 years.

ABOVE
Carl Nielsen, composer of two of this season's mythical works, the *Helios* overture and the 'nature scene' *Pan and Syrinx*

INSET LEFT
The head of Apollo: pediment sculpture (5th century BC) from the Temple of Zeus at Olympia

FAR LEFT
Helios, the Sun-god, drives his chariot across the sky: red-figure vase (Athenian, 5th century BC), on show at the British Museum

BELOW
Apollon musagète: a scene from the Kirov Ballet's current production of Balanchine's 1928 ballet

British Museum (left) National Gallery (right) Lebrecht Music Collection (inset left/bottom right)

... AND ON THE EARTH

Benjamin Britten (1913–76)
Six Metamorphoses after Ovid
PCM 1

No poet suffered a more tragic 'metamorphosis' than Ovid, banished from Rome by the Emperor Augustus to distant exile on the barbaric Black Sea coast. One of the gems of Classical literature, Ovid's *Metamorphoses* retold in Latin verse many Greek myths involving characters who in some way 'changed shape'. For his haunting 1951 solo oboe suite, *Six Metamorphoses after Ovid*, Britten *(above, c1945)* chose half a dozen lively tales: 'Pan' portrays the capricious goat-god from whose lusts a last-minute metamorphosis sometimes offered unfortunate females their only hope of escape; 'Phaeton' follows Helios' son as he falls sizzling from the sky after taking over the reins of his father's chariot; boastful 'Niobe' freezes, bewitchingly, into stone; 'Bacchus' makes Ariadne a bright star in the heavens; 'Narcissus', besotted with his own image, pines away and becomes a flower; and 'Arethusa', fleeing a river-god, turns into a babbling stream. Britten's masterly work embraces every mood from the sad and forlorn to the cheeky and vivacious.

Claude Debussy (1862–1918)
Syrinx
PCM 1

Carl Nielsen (1865–1931)
Pan and Syrinx
PROM 52

Like Britten's *Metamorphoses*, Debussy's *Syrinx* makes ingenious use of an unaccompanied solo instrument to evoke a mythical subject. Initially entitled *Flûte de Pan*, it evokes the same wistful, antique mood as the composer's exquisite *Prélude à L'après-midi d'un faune*, and perfectly captures the fragile delicacy of the Greek maiden who was pursued by the lascivious goat-god Pan before being miraculously transformed into the reed (*syrinx*) from which the ancient Greek pan-pipes took their name.

If Debussy's *Syrinx* reveals the nymph's shy vulnerability, Nielsen's 1918 'nature scene' *Pan and Syrinx* is much breezier – even rumbustious in places – as Pan tortures the poor girl with his clumsy dancing. Opening flutes yield to wild tambourine and cacophonous clarinets as Pan makes his Priapic presence known, positively bursting with passion.

Pan also makes a brief, but decisive, appearance (and enjoys another flute solo) in Ravel's pastoral ballet *Daphnis and Chloë* (Prom 41). But in this case, it's pirates who do the chasing and Pan who saves the chaste nymph Chloë and reunites her with her shepherd lover Daphnis. Premiered in Paris in 1912, Ravel's sensuous score includes one of music's most memorable sunrises.

King Priam – an opera specifically about what its composer called 'the mysterious nature of human choice' – the Trojan king decides to readopt his son Paris, despite the oracles that led to his being condemned, like Oedipus, to be exposed at birth, he consciously sets in train the events that result inevitably in his own death and Troy's downfall.

So with one hand the gods seem to sustain and redeem us (even Oedipus, according to some legends, enjoys a serene old age), while with the other they undermine us. Apollo's gift of prophecy to the Trojan princess Cassandra carries the curse that no-one will believe her, even when she rightly predicts Troy's defeat. Orestes' obedience to Apollo's oracle – which commands him to exact the matricidal revenge that his sister Electra so desperately desires – dooms him to madness and the pursuing Furies. Phaedra's life is torn apart by a head-on collision between her devotion to Artemis, the goddess of chastity, and to Aphrodite, the apostle of free love. 'Do this, but don't' seems to be the rubric of this schizophrenic morality, as it sets human beings at odds both with the divine order and with one another. Meanwhile, the chorus – as in Mendelssohn's incidental music for Sophocles' *Antigone* – struggles to lend moral definition, hymning elusive abstracts like 'Time', 'Law' and 'Justice' or anthropomorphic divinities like Bacchus, Eros and Aphrodite, in a vain attempt to pin down universal principles with which to alter or avoid some impending doom.

ALL CHANGE FOR DAPHNE AND DANAE

Richard Strauss (1864–1949)

An den Baum Daphne
Die Liebe der Danae – Symphonic Fragment
PROM 24

Late in life, Richard Strauss *(right)* wrote two mythological operas that, though less well known than his earlier *Elektra* and *Ariadne on Naxos*, rank among his very best work. *Daphne* is the tale of the nature-loving nymph who begged to be changed into a laurel tree in order to escape the roving-eyed god Apollo. In Strauss's opera, the climactic transformation is described orchestrally, while Daphne sings wordlessly from inside her new bark casing. But a few years after the work's 1938 Dresden premiere, Strauss set to music a further text, entitled *An den Baum Daphne* ('To Daphne, the laurel tree'), which forms a charming pendant to the opera: a setting for mixed chorus and boys' voices, it exudes a calm resignation akin to the composer's glorious *Four Last Songs*.

In the original myth on which Strauss's next (and penultimate) opera, *Die Liebe der Danae* ('The Love of Danae'), is based, a god himself is transformed: Zeus, changing himself into a shower of gold to penetrate Danae's defences (the result of their union being the Gorgon-slaying hero Perseus, whose statue plays a leading role in another of this season's operas, Berlioz's *Benvenuto Cellini*). In Strauss's opera, the golden shower is merely a dream, though Danae herself briefly gets turned into gold, thanks to another suitor's Midas touch. Sadly, Strauss only ever saw a dress rehearsal of *Danae* after Hitler's 1944 declaration of 'Total War' led to the closure of all the Reich's theatres and the cancellation of the scheduled premiere. The opera was not finally staged until 1952, three years after Strauss's death. Shortly afterwards, Clemens Krauss, who had conducted that first performance, arranged a 'Symphonic Fragment' from the opera which he premiered on a visit to London with the Vienna Philharmonic Orchestra. Drawing on the score's final pages, in which Jupiter nobly renounces Danae in favour of his mortal rival, it contains music as ravishing as anything in *Der Rosenkavalier*.

ABOVE
Perseus with the head of the Gorgon, Medusa: bronze statue by Benvenuto Cellini (1500–71) in the Loggia dei Lanzi, Florence

LEFT
A divine dream: *Danae and the Shower of Gold* (1545) by Titian

AKG London (above left/bottom right) British Museum (bottom left) Lebrecht Music Collection (top right/inset right)

ABOVE
André Gide: a 1920s portrait photograph of the French writer (1869–1951) who wrote the text for Stravinsky's *Perséphone* and whose interest in Greek myths also resulted in an Oedipus drama and a Theseus novella

BOTTOM RIGHT
Ida Rubinstein: a 1910 portrait painting by Valentin Serov of the Russian-born dancer and actress (1885–1960) who commissioned *Perséphone*

BELOW
Orpheus playing his lyre: a red-figure vase (Athenian, 5th century BC), on show at the British Museum

TO HELL AND BACK

Igor Stravinsky (1882–1971)
Orpheus
PROM 51

From Jacopo Peri, whose *Euridice* of 1600 was the second opera ever written, to Hector Berlioz, whose early cantata *La mort d'Orphée* (PCM 8) offers hints of a master musician in the making, right through to Sir Harrison Birtwistle, whose long-gestated opera *The Mask of Orpheus* spawned a host of satellite works, including *Nenia: the Death of Orpheus* (Prom 36), and Hans Werner Henze, whose Edward Bond-scripted choral cycle *Orpheus Behind the Wire* (also Prom 36) transplants the myth to the political climate of the early 1980s, composers have been fired by the tale of the legendary Greek musician who ventured down to the realm of the dead to rescue his wife Eurydice, only to look round on their way back home – contrary to his infernal instructions – and lose her for ever.

Like his earlier *Apollon musagète* (see page 14), Stravinsky's serene score for the ballet *Orpheus* – premiered in New York in 1948 with choreography by Balanchine – harks back to French Baroque forms. With a harp entrancingly imitating Orpheus' lyre, the story unfolds 'as if in a dream', though when the hapless singer looks back at his beloved, all hell breaks loose. In the myths, Orpheus came to a sticky end, torn apart by female followers of Dionysus. Stravinsky, however, brings his *Orpheus* to a happier conclusion.

LEFT
Stravinsky's *Orpheus*: Herbert Bliss as Apollo in George Balanchine's 1948 premiere production of the ballet, with sets and costumes designed by Isamu Noguchi

William Schuman (1910–92)
A Song of Orpheus
PROM 7

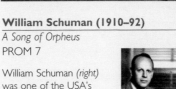

William Schuman (*right*) was one of the USA's major post-war symphonists. A reworking of his 1944 Shakespeare setting 'Orpheus and His Lute', his concertante piece *A Song of Orpheus* was written in 1961 for the great American cellist Leonard Rose and offers a song-like eulogy of the mythical musician, by turns lulling, vigorous and elegiac.

Igor Stravinsky (1882–1971)
Perséphone
PROM 30

A unique hybrid of oratorio, mime, declamation and dance, *Perséphone* was written in 1934 to a commission from the Russian ballerina Ida Rubinstein, on a text by André Gide. The original Homeric myth – an attempt to explain the annual cycle of the seasons – tells how Persephone, daughter of Demeter the earth-mother, is abducted by Hades, god of the underworld. Although her mother eventually secures her release, Persephone has swallowed six pomegranate seeds while in the realm of the dead, and so is doomed to spend six months of every year below ground (Autumn and Winter), only returning to earth for the other six (Spring and Summer), when her presence brings seedtime and harvest to the world.

Perséphone displays none of the brutal violence of Stravinsky's other, better-known treatment of ancient fertility myths, *The Rite of Spring* (Prom 55); instead, its transparent textures exude innocence, purity and charm.

THESEUS AND THE TWO DAUGHTERS OF MINOS

Joseph Haydn (1732–1809)
Arianna a Naxos
PCM 4

Like so many other composers Haydn too wrote an opera on Orpheus, his last, *L'anima del filosofo* (written for London in 1791 but not performed anywhere until 1951). He also wrote a particularly fine concert aria on the subject of Ariadne, the daughter of the Cretan king Minos, who helped the Athenian hero Theseus to overcome her half-brother, the monstrous bull-headed Minotaur. Unhappily, Theseus – one of legend's earliest cads – then abandoned Ariadne on the island of Naxos, where she was later found by Dionysus and, some say, changed by him into a star.

Dating from the year of the French Revolution, Haydn's masterly four-part aria is a touching soliloquy for the forlorn Ariadne. Unaware that Theseus has fled, she seeks vainly for him, but hears only the echoes of her own cries until, spying his departing sail, her fury turns to suicidal desperation.

Jean-Philippe Rameau (1683–1764)
Hippolyte et Aricie – Suite
PROM 33

Long after abandoning Ariadne, Theseus, now king of Athens, married her sister Phaedra. The tragic heroine of plays by Euripides, Seneca and Racine, she conceived an unrequited passion for her handsome but prudish stepson, Hippolytus (Theseus's son by the Amazonian queen he weds in Shakespeare's *A Midsummer Night's Dream*). All ends in tears. First Phaedra kills herself from guilt; then Theseus curses his supposedly incestuous son, bringing about his death in a grisly run-in with a sea-monster (or, in some versions, a bull) – only to learn too late of the lad's innocence. Rameau's first opera *Hippolyte et Aricie* gives the tale a happier twist: Phaedra still dies but Hippolytus survives, and gets to marry his true love, Aricia, as well.

Rameau *(left)* returned to Greek myths for such later operas as *Dardanus*, an apocryphal pre-history of the legendary founder of the royal house of Troy; *Platée*, a comic tale about Jupiter's mock marriage to a marsh-nymph; and *Les Boréades*, in which Apollo sorts out the love-life of a Bactrian queen forced to marry one of the sons of the North Wind. Dances from all three can be heard in Prom 70.

Benjamin Britten (1913–76)
Phaedra
PROM 65

A setting of the American poet Robert Lowell's verse translation of Racine *(right)*, Britten's searing soliloquy *Phaedra* was composed (for Janet Baker) at the end of his life, when failing health made it physically difficult for him to write. He restricted himself therefore to reduced forces, modelling the work on Handel's Italian cantatas, with an orchestra of strings (with added percussion) and a Baroque-style continuo group of cello and harpsichord; the structure too is 18th-century in its five-part sequence of recitatives and arias. But the work is no dry pastiche: a vivid display of torn emotions, like a superb operatic *scena*, it harks back to the vexed yearnings of Elizabeth I in Britten's 1953 Coronation opera *Gloriana*, while the overt eroticism ('I want your sword's spasmodic final inch') was perhaps only possible after Britten had courageously addressed the pederastic longings of Thomas Mann's Von Aschenbach in his final opera, *Death in Venice*. 'I love you! Fool, I love you, I adore you!' cries Phaedra – mythical maybe, but a woman of real flesh and blood.

ABOVE
Samuel Barber

RIGHT
Martha Graham in her 1946
Medea ballet *Serpent Heart*
(later retitled *Cave of the
Heart*), with sets and costumes
designed by Isamu Noguchi

'When I needed a place for
Medea on stage, the heart
of her being, Isamu brought
me a snake. And when I
brooded on what I felt was
the insoluble problem of
representing Medea flying to
return to her father, the Sun,
Isamu devised a dress for me
worked from vibrating brilliant
pieces of bronze wire that
became my garment and
moved with me across the
stage as my chariot of flames'
(Martha Graham, *Blood
Memory*)

In all these earthly goings-on, the
gods' main intermediary was Hermes,
the winged messenger, who, in his
Roman guise of Mercury, shares with
his elemental namesake title-billing in
John Woolrich's new BBC Proms
commission, *Double Mercury* (*see 'New
Music', pages 66–75*). It is Hermes who,
in Tippett's *King Priam*, summons Paris
to his fatal judgement in the beauty
contest between the three goddesses;
and Hermes again who, as the Trojan
king approaches his end ('He already
breathes an air as from another planet'),
unexpectedly bursts into a rapt hymn
in praise of music – 'O divine music,
O stream of sound, in which the states
of soul flow, surfacing and drowning,
while we sit watching from the bank …'
It is Hermes, too, who recalls the errant
Jupiter to Olympus at the end of
Richard Strauss's *Die Liebe der Danae*,
and who in Berlioz's *The Trojans* brings
Aeneas Jove's command to abandon
Dido and leave Carthage for Italy.

Though among the most radical of
19th-century composers, Berlioz's
admiration for Virgil, the poet-laureate
of Augustan Rome, pre-dated his passion
for more overtly Romantic writers like
Shakespeare and Byron. He recalls in
Chapter 2 of his *Memoirs* the blushing
emotion he felt as a boy translating for
his father the story of Dido's doomed
love for Aeneas from Virgil's *Aeneid* –
later the prime source for his text for
The Trojans. Among the first operas he
saw upon his arrival in Paris was
Salieri's myth-based *The Danaids*, while
it was after seeing Gluck's Euripidean
Iphigenia in Tauris that Berlioz finally

determined to abandon medicine and
become a composer.

And of course it's not only operas
and theatre scores that have been
inspired by Greek myths, but ballets,
songs, concert overtures and symphonic
poems. That Sibelius or Nielsen should
turn aside from Nordic saga to write
The Oceanides or the *Helios* overture
might seem surprising. Sometimes such
works spring from chance circumstance:
a first voyage across the Atlantic, a
holiday in Athens respectively. Often,
as with Mendelssohn's *Antigone* music,
they stem from a specific commission.
For Richard Strauss, it was seeing a
Berlin production of Sophocles' *Electra*
in Hugo von Hofmannsthal's translation
that fired him to broach the idea of a
collaboration that was to lead directly
or indirectly to four more operas based
on Greek myths – variously comic or
tragic variations on the tales of Ariadne,
Danae, Daphne and Helen of Troy.

MEDEA, THE SORCERESS

Samuel Barber (1910–81)
Medea's Meditation and Dance of Vengeance
PROM 41

Niece of the enchantress Circe and grandchild of the Sun, Medea is one of Greek myth's
darker characters. A princess of Colchis, she used her magic arts to help Jason steal the
Golden Fleece by bewitching its guardian dragon. Once back in Greece, however, Jason's
ardour for her waned, and he plumped for a lucrative marriage to a rival princess. Medea,
cruelly spurned, turned on her former lover and wreaked havoc upon his family, slaying even
her own two infant sons. Yet, in her crisis, she can still attract our sympathy.

Samuel Barber's ballet version, written for Martha Graham, was first staged in New York
(under the title *Serpent Heart*) in 1946. Best known for his serene *Adagio*, Barber later
extracted an orchestral tone poem from his complete ballet score, focusing on Medea's
sombre brooding and the terrifying revenge she exacts upon Jason's new household.

Two refugees from Diaghilev's Ballets Russes, where the combination of myth and dance was something of a given (compare Nijinsky's Debussyan faun), Stravinsky and the choreographer George Balanchine both liked the idea of a 'mythical' ballet triptych: the result was *Apollon musagète*, *Orpheus* and *Agon* (the latter, strictly speaking, based on the stylised dialogue of Greek tragedy rather than any specific myth).

But Stravinsky was repeatedly drawn to Greek myths throughout his life and besides these three ballets, and a projected further dance piece based on Homer's *Odyssey*, he composed both the melodrama *Perséphone* and the opera-oratorio *Oedipus rex*.

Other 20th-century composers' involvement with Greek mythology seems more sporadic or surprising. If Britten's finest myth-based work, *Phaedra*, was composed near the end of his life, both his 1939 fantasia for piano and strings, *Young Apollo*, and his 1951 oboe solo, *Six Metamorphoses after Ovid*, attest to its enduring power over him. As early as 1930, when he was working with Auden, Isherwood, Spender and MacNeice in the ground-breaking Group Theatre, Britten wrote incidental music for Aeschylus' *Agamemnon*; and soon after returning from the USA, where

ABOVE
An imaginary likeness of the Athenian playwright Sophocles (c496–406 BC): a Hellenistic bronze head from the 2nd century BC, on show at the British Museum

BOTTOM LEFT
Stage design for *Oedipus Rex* by Théodore Stravinsky, the composer's eldest son

OEDIPUS & ANTIGONE: THE TRAGIC TALE OF THE ROYAL HOUSE OF THEBES

Igor Stravinsky (1882–1971)
Oedipus rex
PROM 65

Parricide, incest, suicide and self-mutilation: perhaps no Athenian tragedy has greater impact or has achieved greater fame than Sophocles' *Oedipus rex*. So it was the obvious choice for Stravinsky *(inset top right)* when, in 1925, he conceived the idea of composing a 'monumental' opera in Latin 'on an ancient tragedy with which everyone would be familiar'. For his text he turned to the French poet, playwright and film director Jean Cocteau *(inset bottom right)*, who had already adapted Sophocles' *Antigone* for Arthur Honegger and who was later to rework the

Oedipus legend again in his play *The Infernal Machine* and to base two films on the Orpheus myth. It was Cocteau in turn who had the idea of interspersing the sung Latin sections (wittily translated by a pun-loving Catholic priest) with a spoken narration in the language of the audience – just in case the story of Oedipus' gradual unveiling of his terrible secret wasn't quite as familiar to everyone as all that.

Felix Mendelssohn (1809–47)
Antigone – Music for Sophocles' Tragedy
PROM 8

The final part of Sophocles' 'Theban Trilogy' – three plays that, though not written as a set, chart the rise and fall of Thebes' dysfunctional royal family – *Antigone* tells how, after Oedipus' death, his daughter defies the edict of her uncle, King Creon, and, placing personal conscience above the law, performs the last rites over the corpse of her brother Polynices, which Creon

has ordered to be left unburied for his crime in attacking the city in an attempt to seize the throne. For her act of human charity, Antigone is herself sentenced to be buried alive; and, though Creon eventually relents, his intransigence results in the deaths not just of Antigone, but of his own wife and son as well.

Determined to reform the German stage by banishing farce and pantomime in favour of Shakespeare and the ancient classics, it was the Prussian king Friedrich Wilhelm IV who in 1840 commissioned Mendelssohn to compose music for Sophocles' *Antigone*, and later also for *Oedipus at Colonus* (the central part of the 'Theban Trilogy') and for Aeschylus' *Oresteia* (a project the composer never fulfilled).

Mendelssohn's use of a strophic male chorus here recalls his great biblical oratorios *Elijah* and *St Paul*. In addition to some striking sections of melodrama (with the actors speaking rhythmically over music), the score includes a jubilant Hymn to Bacchus and a buoyant ode praising man's Promethean skills. The King was so delighted with the result he had a special commemorative coin minted. But not everyone was so enthusiastic: the poet Hebbel wrote in his diary that this resplendent music 'suits Sophocles about as well as a waltz suits a sermon'.

BELOW
Felix Mendelssohn

British Museum (top right); Theodore Stravinsky Foundation/Lebrecht Music Collection (left); Lebrecht Music Collection (bottom right/inset top right); AKG, London/Walter Limot (inset bottom right)

FAR RIGHT

The Procession of the Wooden Horse into Troy (c1760) by Giovanni Domenico Tiepolo (1727–1804)

THE TROJAN WAR

Michael Tippett (1905–98)

King Priam
PROM 3

The 10-year siege of Troy inspired the last great saga in Greek mythology: it's the point where legend finally merges into history. Yet, in Homer's epic *Iliad*, we are still firmly in the world of myth, with the gods themselves taking sides in the battles. Not that Homer leaves us in any doubt that, for mortals, war was a terrible ordeal. Michael Tippett *(above)*, a convinced (and convicted) pacifist, shared this view, and in his 1962 opera *King Priam* he underlines the human dilemma of Troy's beleaguered ruler, who – by choosing to spare Paris, the son whom the Fates have destined to bring disaster – virtually wills his own and his city's destruction. Priam's personal tragedy reaches its climax with the death of his oldest son Hector at the hands of the avenging Achilles, and Priam's moving night-time encounter with his bitter enemy as he begs for the return of his son's mutilated corpse is among the most moving moments in a score that is by turns splendid, touching and tender.

BELOW

The death of Priam at the altar of Zeus: a 6th-century BC black-figure Athenian vase, on show at the British Museum

Hector Berlioz (1803–69)

The Trojans – Part 1 'The Capture of Troy'
PROM 47

Not until 21 years after his death was Berlioz's massive five-act opera *The Trojans* finally staged complete (and even then with cuts). Now, in its composer's bicentenary year, *The Trojans* is recognised as not just a marathon, but an operatic masterpiece on a par with Wagner's equally mythic *Ring*. The first two acts, reluctantly repackaged by Berlioz as 'The Capture of Troy', relate the besieged city's final hours. The central character here is not Priam (as in Tippett's opera) but Priam's daughter, the prophetess Cassandra, cursed by Apollo always to foresee the future but never to be believed. Berlioz poignantly depicts the aching tragedy of her situation as she fails first to persuade her lover Corebus to flee the doomed city, then to prevent her fellow Trojans, jubilant at the Greeks' apparent retreat, from dragging the fateful Wooden Horse within the city walls. At the end, as the Greeks overwhelm the burning city, Cassandra leads the Trojan women in an act of mass suicide. But, before then, Hector's ghost has appeared to his cousin Aeneas, the goddess Venus' son, telling him to flee Troy and seek a new future in the West.

Inspired by the classical operas of Gluck and Cherubini, Berlioz's score is one of the most highly charged and dramatic ever written. Yet 'The Capture of Troy' was never staged in the composer's lifetime: 'O my noble, heroic virgin Cassandra, I shall never see you!' he lamented in his diary.

his Auden collaboration *Paul Bunyan* had dealt with another, more recent myth, he composed music for a 1943 BBC radio play, *The Rescue* – based on the story of Penelope in Homer's *Odyssey* – that was to be his most substantial score before his break-through opera *Peter Grimes*. Myths surface too, more or less indirectly, in his operas *The Rape of Lucretia* (1946), *A Midsummer Night's Dream* (1960) and *Death in Venice* (1973), with its dream vision of Apollo and Dionysus; while his 1951 edition of Purcell's *Dido and Aeneas* did much to restore his great precursor's reputation.

From titles alone, one might think that *King Priam* was Tippett's only large-scale sortie into Greek myth. Yet even where he devised his own 'myths', under the influence of Jung, there is a debt to Classical mythology. The germ of his first opera *The Midsummer Marriage* (1955) – a modern-day *Magic Flute* – was sown by a classic Jungian dream in which he beheld an image of 'a wooded hilltop with a temple' and a young girl 'in a costume reminiscent of the goddess Athena' coldly spurning an ardent young man in a costume 'reminiscent of the god Dionysus'. Tippett was quick to recognise the 'collective' Jungian implications of this vision. And, just as Mozart borrowed masonic terminology in *The Magic Flute*, so Tippett, as the two initiates descend from the temple, adapts a quotation from an ancient Orphic tablet that originally offered Dante-esque instructions for entering the House of Hades: 'Say "I am a child of Earth and of Starry Heaven. But my race is of Heaven. Give me quickly the cold

DESTINY'S CALL AND DIDO'S LAMENT

Hector Berlioz (1803–69)

The Trojans – Part 2 'The Trojans at Carthage'
PROM 48

Tragically, the only part of his great opera *The Trojans* that Berlioz ever did hear were its last three acts, retitled *The Trojans at Carthage* and staged in Paris in 1863, albeit with cuts.

Like the opera's first two acts, and unlike Tippett's *King Priam*, Berlioz's tragic tale of the refugee Aeneas' deadly dalliance in North Africa draws upon the Roman poet Virgil's Latin epic *The Aeneid* rather than upon the Greek poet Homer's *Iliad*. But much as Berlioz revered Virgil, he also worshipped Shakespeare, and lent his narrative a truly Shakespearian dimension by intercutting the 'high' tragedy of the Carthaginian queen's suicidal passion for the god-driven Trojan prince with the reactions of 'common' folk swept up in their grand destiny – a young Phrygian sailor sighing for his homeland, a pair of old Trojan sea dogs reluctant to take to sea again. And for the climactic – and ravishing – love-duet, he even took his text from the 'In such a night' speech in *The Merchant of Venice*. 'It's Shakespeare Virgilianised,' as Berlioz boasted to a friend.

While Aeneas is a thrilling role for a tenor, Dido a sizzling mezzo-soprano part, and the orchestration stunning throughout, the opera is especially strong on choral writing:

from the opening Carthaginian national anthem to the exciting 'Royal Hunt and Storm' (with its woodland nymphs and satyrs in full cry), the chorus are close observers of the fate of their wretched and despairing queen, who finally stabs herself to death on a vast funeral pyre as her lover sails blithely away to found a new Troy – Rome – in Italy.

Henry Purcell (1659–95)

Dido and Aeneas
PROM 58

Purcell's *Dido and Aeneas* was written almost two centuries before Berlioz's Virgilian *magnum opus*. Sadly, the old tale that it was first staged in a Chelsea girls' school is now doubtful. But that the composer's sympathies lie with his heroine, pitifully lurching between optimism and despair, rather than with his hero, obsessed with his own destiny, is in no doubt, from Dido's poignant first words ('Ah, Belinda, I am prest with torment!') to the wonderful repeated bass line of her final suicide aria ('When I am laid in earth'), one of the most moving solos in all opera.

LEFT
Aeneas Telling Dido of the Misfortunes of Troy (1815) by Baron Pierre Narcisse Guérin (1774–1833)

BELOW
Title-page from an 1892 French edition of Part 2 of Berlioz's opera *The Trojans*

INSET LEFT
Henry Purcell: a 1690 portrait in the National Portrait Gallery attributed to Sir Godfrey Kneller

water flowing forth from the Lake of Memory" ... And thereafter among the other heroes thou shalt have lordship.' So *The Midsummer Marriage* harks back directly to Greek myth via the Orphic fertility and resurrection rites of the ancient Eleusinian Mysteries. Tippett was to quote this mystic text once more in his last, and ostensibly space-age, opera *New Year* (1989). So Orpheus survives not just in a post-Freudian age, but in the Sci-Fi era too.

And, as the 21st century gets under way, there's no sign that myth's power to inspire music is diminishing. With each new retelling, as the ancient Athenian tragedians recognised with their

successive reworkings of the same few canonic tales, our appreciation of the great Greek myths is freshly challenged and heightened, deepened and intensified.

In their 1949 opera *The Olympians* JB Priestley and Arthur Bliss revived a medieval French fable which held that the Greek gods are not dead but live on, disguised as a group of strolling players, manifesting themselves in their full glory only once a year, on Midsummer's Day. One can take that further. Every time we retell the story of Prometheus' theft of fire, of Zeus' amorous adventures or of the sack of Troy, every time we listen to Beethoven's *Prometheus*, Strauss's *Danae* or Berlioz's *The Trojans*, the gods and myths of ancient Greece come alive again and are enriched and revitalised for a new age.

A CYCLE OF REVENGE

Richard Strauss (1864–1949)
Elektra
PROM 15

Although the Greeks won the war, a grim fate befell many of the victors. Odysseus famously spent 10 years struggling back to Ithaca, only to find his own house and wife under siege. Idomeneus, King of Crete, nearly died at sea on his way home and only saved his life with an ill-advised vow to Neptune, the near-tragic results of which drive the plot of Mozart's early operatic masterpiece *Idomeneo* (Prom 34). As for Agamemnon, the Greek commander-in-chief, the worst fate of all awaited him upon his return to Mycenae – butchered in his bath by his own wife, Clytemnestra, and her new lover, Aegisthus. But his daughter, the princess Electra, bided her time until, finally reunited with her exiled brother Orestes, she turned the tables on her mother and her lover and slew them both in cold blood.

Dominated by its striking writing for female voices – principally the ruthless Electra herself and her monstrous mother – Strauss's harrowing and bloody opera *Elektra* (premiered in Dresden in 1909) is, like Stravinsky's *Oedipus Rex* and Mendelssohn's *Antigone*, based on a play by Sophocles and boasts a score that, to quote press reports of its 1910 London premiere, is quite simply 'Elektrifying'!

23

listening to musicians – responding to their needs

For people in the music business there is always help at hand from the Musicians Benevolent Fund

- Help with stress and health problems
- Help and advice with financial problems
- Help that's given in strict confidence
- Help given to outstanding young musicians

We operate throughout England, Scotland, Wales and the whole of Ireland

If you or someone you know needs our help, please contact:

Musicians Benevolent Fund
16 Ogle Street
London W1W 6JA

Tel: 020 7636 4481
Facsimile: 020 7637 4307

email: info@mbf.org.uk
website: www.mbf.org.uk

Reg. Charity No.228089

EXPLORE THE
MASTERPIECES OF
CLASSICAL MUSIC
IN DEPTH

THE BBC PROMS
POCKET GUIDE TO
GREAT CONCERTOS

edited by Nicholas Kenyon

THE BBC PROMS
POCKET GUIDE TO
GREAT SYMPHONIES

edited by Nicholas Kenyon

As heard on the BBC

BBC

WITH
THE BBC PROMS
POCKET GUIDES

The accessible
and authoritative guides
to the best in classical music

OUT NOW IN PAPERBACK

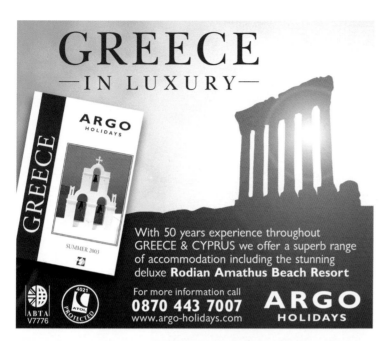

Living with the best

Until now, finding one system to provide the best quality sound and the perfect video picture has been difficult.

At Meridian Audio we have the solution. We make what is recognised as the world's finest audio and video system for the home. All our products from CD/DVD players to

the latest in digital loudspeakers work as a matched system controlled from one handset so you can have the best of both worlds – performance without compromise.

From the inventors of MLP, mandatory coding system for DVD-Audio, Meridian Audio – the best!

BOOTHROYD STUART
MERIDIAN

Meridian Audio Limited
Stonehill, Stukeley Meadows
Huntingdon, England PE29 6EX
Tel (0)1480 445678 Fax (0)1480 445686

www.meridian-audio.com

Our thanks to the University of Cambridge, Faculty of Music, West Road, Cambridge.

CHANDOS

CHANDOS ARTISTS AT THE 2003 PROMS

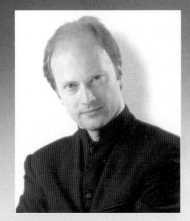

Gianandrea Noseda

Leonard Slatkin

Richard Hickox

Rumon Gamba

BBC *Symphony* Orchestra

BBC National Orchestra of Wales / Cerddorfa Genedlaethol Gymreig y **BBC**

BBC *Concert* ORCHESTRA

Chandos Records Ltd, Chandos House, Commerce Way, Colchester, Essex CO2 8HQ, UK
Telephone: 01206 225200 • E-mail: enquiries@chandos.net • Website: www.chandos.net

BERLIOZ

HECTOR BERLIOZ (1803–69)

On the bicentenary of the composer's birth, David Cairns **charts his posthumous progress from the margins to the mainstream**

'Will you believe that I have fallen in love, *utterly in love*, with my Queen of Carthage?' (Berlioz writing to a friend in 1856, a year into the composition of *The Trojans*)

ABOVE
French contralto Marie Delna (1875–1932) as Dido, the role in which she made her Paris Opéra debut at the age of 17

LEFT
Hector Berlioz: a 19th-century stone copy of the 1890 bronze sculpture by Alfred Lenoir, which stands in the main square of the composer's birthplace, La Côte Saint-André, and was itself based on a photograph taken in 1863

RIGHT
Roman Carnival: costume design for the 1838 Paris premiere of *Benvenuto Cellini*

If the original organisers of the Proms, a hundred and more years ago, could see the prospectus for 2003, they would not be surprised to find the 'Hungarian March' from *The Damnation of Faust* among the items in 'The Nation's Favourite Prom' – the piece was performed seven times in the opening season. (The *Damnation* itself was a favourite of Victorian choral societies, even if, in the words of Bernard Shaw, they did their best to 'tame' the work and 'stuff the composer into a frock coat and stick a hymn-book in his hand'.) What would startle those first Proms planners would be to find half a dozen of the composer's major works featured throughout the season.

Berlioz has come a long way in the intervening century. The bicentenary of his birth sees him nearer to being fully recognised than ever before. The composer who seemed destined to remain on the margins of musical history, an eternal outsider, a fascinating footnote rather than a truly great artist, is coming into his kingdom.

This is not the place to go in detail into the reasons why he was excluded and why he is no longer – what causes combined to make his music difficult to accept, and what has now changed. But one obvious factor is that the bursting-

open of the repertory, due partly to the advent of recording, has brought about a fundamental change in the way we look at the music of the past.

There is no longer a dominant style, as there was 100 years ago, and indeed much more recently: the Anglo-German 'mainstream'. Instead there is a multiplicity of styles, all admissible – something that would have delighted Berlioz, who didn't believe in orthodoxies or dogmas of any kind (the only '-ism' he subscribed to was pluralism). His music (like Bruckner's) is no longer judged by criteria irrelevant to it. It can at last be considered on its own terms. And, thanks to recording and far more frequent and more accurate, idiomatic performances, it can become familiar, no longer more pontificated about than actually known. The advances in orchestral virtuosity mean that even a score as difficult to play as *Benvenuto Cellini*, with its knife-edge rhythms and kaleidoscopic changes of colour, becomes manageable.

Those first Proms planners would also be surprised by the number of conductors engaged to do the Berlioz works on the prospectus. That of course is one of the crucial differences between the Proms then and now – no longer a single orchestra and conductor but many – but it has particular significance in

this case. Conductors with a feeling for a composer's style are essential, if that composer's music is to flourish. Partly as a consequence of the Berlioz renaissance, partly as a cause, there are far more today who have an understanding of his music and are keen to perform it than there have ever been before. Six of them are involved in this year's Proms: Colin Davis, Roger Norrington and John Eliot Gardiner (both of whom, at the start of their careers, performed under Davis's baton in Chelsea Opera Group concerts in the 1960s), Mark Elder, Yan Pascal Tortelier and Valery Gergiev.

Even without a complete *Damnation* or *Romeo and Juliet* (excerpts from both of which will be given in scaled-down form by that intriguing Parisian chamber ensemble, Carpe Diem), the range of works on offer is impressive, covering three decades of Berlioz's career, from the Prix de Rome cantatas *La mort d'Orphée* (1827) and *La mort de Cléopâtre* (1829) – imperfectly realised inspirations but containing striking inventions – to his crowning achievement, the epic five-act opera *The Trojans*.

The choice shows the extraordinary diversity of his music. Berlioz is Protean, like Mozart. He never repeats himself – partly no doubt on principle, but still more because he cannot. In an imagination as vivid and complete as his, each work

Bridgeman Art Library/Private Collection (left) Lebrecht Music Collection (above) AKG London (right)

inhabits its unique poetic world, which requires its own distinct colour and atmosphere, and also its own form created afresh in response to the demands of the work in question.

This last was a lesson that he learnt from Beethoven, the encounter with whose symphonies at the Conservatoire concerts in 1828–30 was the single most important discovery of the young Berlioz's musical education. As he listened to the 'Eroica', the Fifth, the 'Pastoral' and the Seventh, and studied them and the score of the Ninth, he saw the endless variety of compositional procedure that was Beethoven's response to the 'poetic idea' embodied in each musically self-sufficient work; he grasped the truth that the symphony was a form of drama as real in its way as the drama of characters in a theatre.

Out of that revelation sprang the five-movement autobiographical *Symphonie fantastique* of 1830 (on whose manuscript score Berlioz wrote Victor Hugo's lines that speak of 'the book of my heart inscribed on every page'). Four years later came his second symphony, *Harold in Italy*, an exuberant musical transformation of Berlioz's wanderings in the mountains east of Rome; and two years after that his 'opera semi-seria' based on the memoirs of 'that bandit of genius', Benvenuto Cellini. *Cellini* takes still further the rhythmic and sonic innovations of *Harold* and its mood of celebration. Even in the revisions that Berlioz made for Liszt's 1852 production at Weimar (a version

less commonly heard nowadays than the original, composed for the Paris Opéra), it is a work of astonishing originality.

It would be hard to find a greater contrast than between it and the gentle, tender oratorio *The Childhood of Christ* (1854), in which Berlioz relived the story of Jesus' birth and childhood as it had stamped itself, in all its vividness and holy intensity, on his boyhood imagination. This was the work that got him back to composing after a lull caused by profound discouragement at the apparently insurmountable difficulty and cost of making his way in Paris. Eighteen months later, in 1856, he took up again the six songs for voice and piano that comprise *Les nuits d'été* (1841) and completed their orchestration, making what seems to be the first-ever orchestral song-cycle – a moving anatomy of romantic love in its many aspects.

As with parts of *The Childhood of Christ*, this is a Berlioz who is not dependent on huge numbers for making an effect (as the old legend had it) but can do so with the most modest means. That can also be true of his grandest works, in which, just as Mahler does, he can reduce his forces to chamber-music

dimensions: think of Andromache's mime scene in Act 1 of *The Trojans*, for solo clarinet and muted strings, or of Hylas' song in Act 5, scored for divided cellos and a handful of wind instruments.

It is apt that this season's Berlioz bicentenary programmes culminate in *The Trojans* (1858). It is his masterpiece; and, more than anything, it was the revelation of the work's beauty and power, at Covent Garden in 1957, that precipitated the whole modern Berlioz revival whose fruits we can now enjoy.

'Oh, my dear Ferrand, I wish I could make you hear the scene where Cleopatra reflects upon the greeting her ghost will get from the shades of the Pharaohs entombed in the Pyramids. It is terrible, frightful!' (Berlioz writing to a friend in 1829)

ABOVE LEFT
The Death of Cleopatra (c1660) by Guido Cagnacci (1606–63)

BELOW
Berlioz stands before a placard listing all his major works with the exception of the unstaged *Trojans*, a poster for which he holds hopefully in his hand: a contemporary cartoon by 'Carjat'

Berlioz at the Proms 2003

Prom 2	The Damnation of Faust – Hungarian March
Prom 12	Les nuits d'été
Prom 14	The Childhood of Christ
Prom 29	Harold in Italy
Prom 39	Benvenuto Cellini
Prom 42	La mort de Cléopâtre
Prom 43	Symphonie fantastique
Prom 47	The Trojans: Part 1
Prom 48	The Trojans: Part 2
Prom 73	Overture 'Roman Carnival'
PCM 8	La mort d'Orphée – monologue; The Damnation of Faust – excerpts; Romeo and Juliet – excerpts

RAF Tour

Bangalore, India – 2 January

Jersey, Channel Islands – 4 February

New Zealand – 1 March

Japan – 20 March

Gibraltar – 15 April

Falkland Islands – 18 May

Madrid, Spain – 1 June

Washington, USA – 15 July

Denmark – 3 August

**Buckingham Palace
(Changing the Guard) – 2 September**

**Edinburgh Castle
(Military Tattoo) – 4 October**

Rome, Italy – 21 November

Paris, France – 15 December

Join the Royal Air Force band and be on the road and in the air 365 days a year.

The RAF values every individual's unique contribution, irrespective of race, ethnic origin, religion, gender, sexual orientation or social background.

rafmusic.co.uk

0845 601 5409 **RAF** ◎

PROKOFIEV

SERGEY PROKOFIEV (1891–1953)

Half a century after the composer's death, David Nice **searches for the real face behind Prokofiev's paradoxical public persona**

ABOVE

An ambivalent portrait of tyranny: Nikolay Cherkasov as the paranoid Tsar in one of the two colour reels from the second part of Eisenstein's expressionist masterpiece *Ivan the Terrible*, banned on Stalin's orders and not seen until five years after the dictator's death

LEFT

Sergey Prokofiev at work at the piano

RIGHT

Galina Ulanova and Yuri Zhdanov as the tragic lovers in the Bolshoy Ballet version of *Romeo and Juliet*

In his first public incarnation as the devilish young composer-pianist of pre-revolutionary St Petersburg, Sergey Prokofiev led one of his wealthy patrons to remark that the young man couldn't bear to hear two true notes in succession 'because his piano is out of tune and he's used to it'. Yet the violinist David Oistrakh, hearing Prokofiev play several of his earlier pieces many years later, was moved to note that in such pieces as the *Visions fugitives* 'the tempestuous, defiant Prokofiev … became as touching as a child'. The tender lyric vein would be ignored for many years to come, and Prokofiev was stuck with that inescapable tag of *enfant terrible* – the naughty boy who never grew up. Now we know different, and in the rainbow of works featured throughout the Proms in this 50th anniversary year of his death heart and soul reign triumphant.

Original melody, which Prokofiev always regarded as much the most important element in music, provides the golden thread through the labyrinth of his early pieces, a breath of fresh air in the Russia of the early 1900s at a time when Glazunov's conservative symphonies dominated the musical skyline and the harmonic mannerisms of Skryabin provided the only innovation. A string of memorable ideas, brimful of

that 'personality' which Stravinsky believed to be Prokofiev's greatest asset, holds together the athletic First Piano Concerto, which was his first star vehicle, and the Third, which became his calling card in America and central Europe. In the more deliberately complicated works he composed in the West during the 1920s and early 1930s – culminating in the often-overlooked *Symphonic Song* of 1934 and, to a lesser extent, the Cello Concerto begun in the same year but not completed until 1938 – rich and original themes often sweat under thick orchestral textures and complicated counterpoint; listen through several times and finally, as the composer himself noted from a later perspective, 'the outlines of a real face emerge'. The face takes on more clearly defined features in the works for a wider audience that Prokofiev composed in Soviet Russia during the last 17 years of his life; however flimsy the context – as in the case of his last full-length ballet *The Stone Flower* – those features remain very much Prokofiev's own.

Yet there are layers and contradictions, as much in Prokofiev's life as in his music; fire and ice remain the irreconcilable poles. 'Cold' is one adjective often applied to the

man and his music, to which anyone familiar only with *Romeo and Juliet* might rightly raise an eyebrow. But Prokofiev could be distant or unsympathetic. His upbringing as an adored only child on the Ukrainian country estate managed by his father, where he was 'little master' to the local children he played with, led to a singularity, if not a superiority, that was compounded by the anomaly at the St Petersburg Conservatory whereby he was much the youngest student in the classes of Lyadov and Rimsky-Korsakov. At large in the Paris of the 1920s, and still battling for recognition, he could be outrageously rude to unwelcome acquaintances.

His extensive correspondence, however, reveals as many facets to his personality as there are voices for the gallery of humanity in his stage works. Paradoxes persist in the gulf between what he said and what he did or felt.

Writing to a literary friend about *The Fiery Angel*, his 1920s opera of demonic possession in the Middle Ages, he mentions 'the empty and terrifying dead end to which magic eventually leads'; yet his genuinely disturbing score reveals him in thrall to that magic. An ardent chess and bridge player who wanted to eliminate all elements of chance in the games at which he excelled, he took a surprisingly large number of risks in his travels across turbulent Russia and central Europe in the First World War and after the Revolution, culminating in a 1918 reconnaissance trip to America that divorced him from his homeland for nine years. In 1936, prompted by the tenets of his Christian Science faith not to fear 'too much success', he made the biggest gamble of all – to move with his family to the Soviet Union, where the interests of a wide musical public, commissions and guaranteed working time all promised to greet him.

Because, unlike Shostakovich, he did not have the relative good fortune to outlive the terrors of the Stalin years (dying on the same day

as the great dictator), and so never had a chance to set the record straight, he was taken too literally on the few occasions when he ventured to explain his music. Declaring his Fifth Symphony in a radio broadcast to be 'a symphony of the greatness of the human spirit', he has been taken at his word ever since; the coincidence of its first performance, which he himself conducted in January 1945, with a major Soviet victory over the Germans quickly reinforced the myth. Yet listen to the violent arming-process of the first movement, or the vicious ripping-to-shreds of the noble melodies in the finale, and 'greatness of spirit' is not the overwhelming impression. The Sixth Symphony, completed two years later, unambiguously projects a broken, dislocated tragedy, and yet Prokofiev described it for a Soviet newspaper in 1947 in the same bland terms. Clearly neither official statement was intended for those who had ears to hear.

That Prokofiev could manage the dark he dared not discuss, as well as the light, became increasingly apparent in the works of his last years, dogged by illness and fear. Although he added patriotic ballast to the later scenes of his operatic masterpiece *War and Peace*, he refused to remove or alter its scenes of devastation and heavy satire. After the straightforward patriotic narrative of

Alexander Nevsky, his first film score for Sergey Eisenstein, the richer, deeper music he wrote for the director's two-part epic *Ivan the Terrible* reflected its move from an essentially celebratory Part 1 to a black depiction of the Tsar's later years in Part 2 that could be taken as a mirror to Stalin's rule (and was, hastening Eisenstein's untimely end). Another great film director, Ingmar Bergman, has expressed his fear of ending up making 'Bergman movies' in the way that Fellini eventually 'did' Fellini. Prokofiev never, when it mattered, ended up writing a 'Prokofiev score'; standing outside the laws of fashion or the modishness of evanescent new works – 'one-day butterflies', as he called them – he is always self-renewing, but always splendidly himself.

LEFT
Stalin's portrait overshadows a scene of 'patriotic ballast' in English National Opera's 2001 production of *War and Peace*

BELOW
Sergey Eisenstein, the great Soviet film director for whom Prokofiev wrote his scores for *Alexander Nevsky* and *Ivan the Terrible*

English National Opera (left) AKG London

symphony hall
birmingham

'Symphony Hall never fails to surprise the ears and delight the spirits'
The Times, February 2001

'an inspiration to the orchestra...an inspiration also to its audiences'
The Times

2003

'The best concert hall in the country'
Daily Telegraph

box office 0121 780 3333

online box office www.symphonyhall.co.uk/boxoffice

www.symphonyhall.co.uk   admin tel: +44 (0)121 200 2000

fax: +44 (0)121 212 1982 email: symphonyhall@necgroup.co.uk

LIGETI

GYÖRGY LIGETI (born 1923)

As the Hungarian master turns 80, Paul Griffiths **celebrates his magical talent for producing music that continues to surprise and delight us**

ABOVE
Tasmin Little, who plays Ligeti's Violin Concerto with Sir Simon Rattle and his Berliner Philharmoniker in Prom 55

LEFT
György Ligeti: 'off in his own world of luminosity and strangeness'

Guy Vivien (left) Clive Barda (above)

Magicians are ageless. György Ligeti has his 80th birthday this year, on 28 May, but he is also as old as the eight minutes of his choral piece *Lux aeterna*, or the unending sounds of his orchestral *Lontano*, or the split-second, snap-crackle events and silences of his musical comic strip *Aventures* and its sequel *Nouvelles aventures*, to mention just some of the pieces being played at this year's Proms.

The spirit of this music is fresh. Each work comes from nowhere and then grows into something never heard before, like an exotic plant or a weird machine – an effect due partly to its magician-composer's command of imagination and surprise, partly to its craftsman-musician's ability to perfect every gesture, every sound. Ligeti is there in what he does, and all of him is there. His music is as various as a human being can be: full of grand plans that often go awry (and usually thereby give rise to still grander plans); emotionally forthcoming much of the time, but also with a capacity for being serenely cryptic; contradictory in lots of other ways (giving and demanding, adventurous and nostalgic, clear and mysterious); and in everything thoroughly individual.

At the same time – in the same sounds – this music is the story of an epoch. To be 80 and Hungarian-Jewish is to have lived through two of the 20th century's great disasters: fascism, and the fiercely corrupted form of socialism that came soon after. Ligeti survived both (though family members and friends did not), and survival became his music's way of life. He found, in what music too had experienced since 1900, if not disasters then immense upheavals: the collapse of traditional tonality, the disappearance of the standard forms, the opening-up to folk music and cultures on other continents. His music would survive these, come through the other side. To do so it would need what he himself surely needed as a Jew under the Nazis and as a freethinker under the Communists: inner strength. And it would gain that inner strength from counterpoint – from lucidity and resilience in the relationship of one line with another.

Ligeti in his twenties – studying and then teaching at the academy of music in Budapest, and composing piano and choral music all the time – made himself a master of the contrapuntal arts, as displayed in Renaissance music, in Bach and in Bartók. As a result, his music has excellent bone structure. Its essential lines, which may be tangled over with any amount of complication, are sure;

its fine detail, which one might need an aural microscope to detect within these lustrous surfaces, is exquisitely efficient. The magic, as always, comes from knowledge as well as illusion.

Having made himself once as a composer, in post-war Hungary, Ligeti had to make himself a second time after leaving Budapest in 1956, following the Soviet invasion. He became a student again, now learning from Western contemporaries whose music he had only dimly heard on jammed radio broadcasts: Karlheinz Stockhausen, Pierre Boulez, Mauricio Kagel. But he was now, in his mid-thirties, complete as an artist, and when he emerged from his study period, in the early 1960s, his music was far from the avant-garde norms of the time, off in its own world of luminosity and strangeness. There it has continued, through a widening range of references and options. His Violin Concerto, finished in 1993, is as wondrous as his *San Francisco Polyphony* from 20 years before, and as well-functioning as the music he was writing more than half a century ago. It also glistens with all a master's sorcery.

Ligeti at the Proms 2003

Prom 18	Lontano
Prom 27	San Francisco Polyphony
Prom 28	Aventures;
	Nouvelles aventures
Prom 36	Lux aeterna
Prom 55	Violin Concerto
PCM 1	Six Bagatelles; Ten Pieces
PCM 3	Horn Trio

BBC
Symphony
Orchestra

Leonard Slatkin Chief Conductor

'No London orchestra
sounds better than
today's BBC Symphony'

2003-2004 Barbican Season

Join the BBC Symphony Orchestra
at the Barbican for a magnificent
season of concerts

Opera
Ligeti *Le grand macabre**
Barber *Vanessa* with Christine Brewer

A celebration of the 75th anniversary of the BBC Symphony Chorus
Berlioz *L'enfance du Christ*, in Westminster Cathedral
Honegger *Le Roi David*

Other stunning vocal concerts including
Strauss *Four Last Songs* with Karita Mattila
Mahler Songs from *Des Knaben Wunderhorn* with Marjana Lipovšek

Other highlights
Mozart Clarinet Concerto with Julian Bliss;
Piano Concertos Nos 20 and 21 with Emanuel Ax
and Stephen Hough

Bruch and **Bartók** Violin Concertos with
Leila Josefowicz and Leonidas Kavakos

Peter Maxwell Davies Composer Portrait

John Cage A weekend focusing on his life and work

Finnish Festival A mini-weekend of concerts
and events

New music from Sally Beamish, Unsuk Chin,
Vic Hoyland, Magnus Lindberg, Kaija Saariaho,
Cindy McTee, Poul Ruders & Joseph Schwantner

Conducted by Leonard Slatkin, Jukka-Pekka Saraste,
Sir Andrew Davis, John Adams, Jiří Bělohlávek,
Michael Boder, Martyn Brabbins, Rumon Gamba,
David Robertson

Become a BBC Symphony Orchestra subscriber and save money
on ticket prices. Call the Barbican Box Office for a free copy of
our season brochure with full details of all concerts (available
in May) or visit our website at www.bbc.co.uk/orchestras/so

barbican

Box Office
020 7638 8891 (bkg fee)
www.barbican.org.uk
Reduced booking fee online

Tickets £16 £12 £8
* Different ticket prices apply

BBC RADIO 90-93FM

Other Anniversary Composers

We also mark the anniversaries of nine other composers, both past and present, who were born or died between 50 and 350 years ago

Novosti London (Spartacus) Ronald Grant Archive (Oliver Twist) Schirmer (Musgrave) Richard E Smith (Saxton) Lebrecht Music Collection (all other photographs)

BORN: 1653

Arcangelo Corelli (1653–1713)

Concerti grossi in D major, Op. 6 No. 4, and G minor, Op. 6 No. 8, 'Christmas Concerto'
Prom 6

BORN: 1903

Lennox Berkeley (1903–89)

Magnificat, Op. 71
Prom 61

BORN: 1903

Aram Khachaturian (1903–78)

Spartacus – Suite No. 2
Prom 2

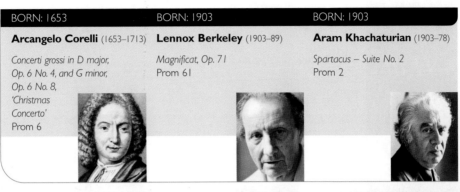

DIED: 1903

Hugo Wolf (1860–1903)

Songs
PCM 4
Italian Serenade
PCM 6

DIED: 1953

Arnold Bax (1883–1953)

November Woods
Prom 17
Oliver Twist – excerpts
Prom 38

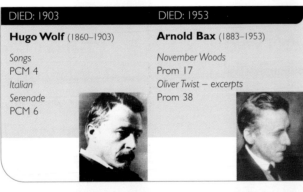

Above: A scene from the 1958 Bolshoy Ballet production of *Spartacus*, with music by Aram Khachaturian

Left: 'Please, sir, I want some more': John Howard Davies in David Lean's 1948 film of *Oliver Twist*, with music by Arnold Bax

95TH BIRTHDAY

Elliott Carter (born 1908)

Clarinet Concerto
Prom 28
Boston Concerto
Prom 35

75TH BIRTHDAY

Thea Musgrave (born 1928)

Helios
Prom 51

70TH BIRTHDAY

Krzysztof Penderecki (born 1933)

Sinfonietta for strings
Prom 32

50TH BIRTHDAY

Robert Saxton (born 1953)

Five Motets
Prom 62
Sonata for Solo Cello on a Theme of Sir William Walton
PCM 7

barbican

"The Barbican Hall is where London's most interesting musical life happens"

SUNDAY TIMES

Box Office
0845 120 7534 (bkg fee)
www.barbican.org.uk
Reduced booking fee online

Mostly Mozart

10 July - 2 August 2003

After a hugely successful inaugural festival last year Mostly Mozart returns to the Barbican featuring talks, films, fireworks and concerts by some of the world's leading young artists.
Featured artists this year include:

Magdalena Kožená

Jonathan Lemalu

Nicholas Daniel

Chloë Hanslip

Academy of St Martin in the Fields

The Sixteen

Jane Glover

Mark Padmore

Garsington Opera

Emma Johnson

Great Performers
2003·2004

September 2003 - June 2004

The Barbican's international classical music series returns this autumn with its best season ever. Artists include:

Vienna Philharmonic

Maxim Vengerov

Bernard Haitink

Gabrieli Consort and Players

Valery Gergiev

Les Arts Florissants

Andreas Scholl

Royal Concertgebouw Orchestra

Cecilia Bartoli

Alfred Brendel

Philadelphia Orchestra

For free brochures with full details of all these concerts call the Barbican Box Office on **0845 120 7534** or email your full postal address to **musicinfo@barbican.org.uk** (quoting 'Proms').
Alternatively visit **www.barbican.org.uk/music**

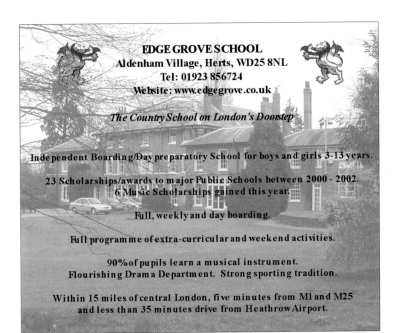

*I*nhabiting the onetime mansion of the Dukes of Buckingham and Chandos, in an incomparable setting of 750 acres of Capability Brown landscape garden and parkland, Stowe is a renowned and vibrant Public School. Our clear vision is to encourage intellectual discovery and promote individuality, not slavish conformity, within a structured, caring and disciplined environment.

Boys are admitted at 13 and 16 years and girls are welcomed into the 6th form; all flourish within our proven house and tutor system. We are proud that our community thrives on an ethos where pupils range from Oxbridge to the intellectually average, and where we score particularly well in 'added value' achievement. The breadth and flexibility of Stowe's academic curriculum reflects the international community through emphasis on communication skills, European awareness, languages and IT. There is also a strong record in the sciences, while Art, Music and Drama are particularly renowned. Pupils are expected to live life to the full, while remaining mindful of others: Stowe celebrates youth rather than stifling it.

We invite you to come and meet the people who are encouraged to exceed their own expectations and who help make Stowe School a unique and sublime host for a 21st century education.

Please contact the Admissions Department, Stowe School
Telephone: +44 (0) 1280 818000   Fax: +44 (0) 1280 818181
email: enquiries@stowe.co.uk   www.stowe.co.uk   Registered Charity No: 310639

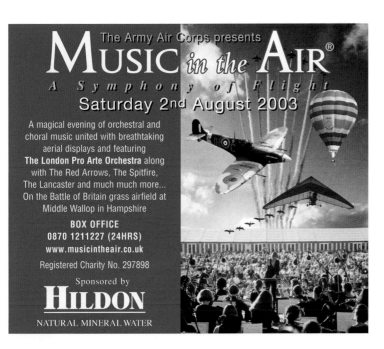

JOHANN STRAUSS II Die Fledermaus

As Glyndebourne's new production wings its way to the Proms, Patrick O'Connor **follows the unstoppable flight of Johann Strauss's** *Bat* **from Viennese vaudeville theatre to the opera houses of the world**

ABOVE
Johann Strauss II

FAR RIGHT
'The Bat' goes international: a selection of English and French sheet-music covers

Although the French, English, German and even Italian comic-opera traditions all have a fair claim to have invented the style that led to operetta, the Austrians can rest assured that it was Johann Strauss II who came up with the formula for the most successful operetta of all time. There has probably never been a month since April 1874, when *Die Fledermaus* received its premiere in Vienna, that this revengers' comedy hasn't been in production somewhere in the world.

The allure of *Die Fledermaus* (which translates, less alluringly, as 'The Bat' – don't ask!) lies in its combination of frivolity and cruelty, with a story that should offend morality, but that ends in laughter. Unlike so many other operettas of the 1860s and 1870s, it isn't a satire on mythology or history, but a contemporary domestic drama with ordinary characters. What better subjects than alcoholism, marital infidelity, tax evasion and master–servant problems with which to poke fun not just at society, but at the very people who were occupying the stalls at the Theater an der Wien?

It wasn't the plot or characters, of course, that rooted *Die Fledermaus* in the world's affections. Strauss made it a work that was as much about dance as song. The Waltz King of Vienna could do just as well with the polka, *csárdás*, galop and military march, and every aria, duet and ensemble in *Die Fledermaus* is in its way a little masterpiece. Even when the operetta wasn't being staged somewhere, Strauss made sure that no-one would forget it, by using some of its main themes in one of his greatest concert waltzes, *Du und Du*.

Opera houses began to take up *Die Fledermaus* even during Strauss's lifetime, and it was the first operetta to become a staple not only in Vienna, but in Berlin, Paris, New York and Moscow. In the 20th century, it was the first operetta ever to be heard at Covent Garden – in 1930, with Lotte Lehmann as Rosalinde. Even while it was enshrined as a classic, *Die Fledermaus* was often dressed up in new formats by canny producers: *Nightbirds* in London, *The Merry Countess* in New York, *La Tsigane* in Paris and *Waltz Time*, an early 'talkie', all sought to cash in on its appeal.

It seems only proper that *Die Fledermaus* should be the first operetta to enter Glyndebourne's stage repertory. The work has always been a favourite with discerning conductors, and Vladimir Jurowski, the Sussex festival's new music director, is but the latest to add his name to a list that stretches back through Erich Kleiber, Bruno Walter and Richard Strauss, even to Gustav Mahler, who conducted a performance at which the composer himself was present.

At the time of Strauss's death, Guido Adler wrote, 'Strauss's melodies strengthen the feeling of home for Viennese, for Austrians. One could say, "Vienna lives in his sounds." They are the musical reflection of the Viennese soul.'

Johann Strauss II • Die Fledermaus
Prom 23 Monday 4 August, 7.00pm

POULENC La voix humaine

It's for you! Rodney Milnes **tempts us to listen in to one side of a French telephone call that all too painfully spells out the end of the** *affaire*

Poulenc's setting of Jean Cocteau's 1928 monodrama was written for his muse, the soprano Denise Duval, and first performed in 1959. It is about the end of a relationship. The protagonist, Elle, has what will be her last conversation with the man who has left her for another woman – a conversation conducted on the telephone, of which we obviously hear only one side. Some matters are comparatively mundane but no less painful for that: which of them will keep the love letters, and what is to become of them; how to arrange for a dog that prefers the man to be returned to him. One is reminded of Mimì's Farewell in *La bohème*.

Other concerns are more obviously traumatic, not least the lies that lovers tell each other, even in these final stages. Elle, initially pretending to be in control, admits that she has lied about the smart clothes she is wearing, about her friend Marthe coming round to cheer her up. She is, and has been, utterly alone. Is she perhaps lying when she describes her suicide attempt, just to give the man a really hard time?

The innocent-seeming text is full of such ambiguities. He is certainly lying when he says that he is ringing from home – we later discover that he's out at a night club. Is the woman interrupting Elle on a crossed line perhaps his new mistress? In just 40 minutes Cocteau and Poulenc manage to invest what is, on the surface, a commonplace situation with extraordinary resonance.

Commonplace or no, the subject-matter of a human being at the end of her tether cannot help but strike a chord in the heart of every listener. Lines like 'I am not used to sleeping alone', or 'Don't worry, one doesn't commit suicide twice', or Elle's request that he and his new mistress don't go to the same hotel that they used to go to – commonplace, but heart-rending.

What has emerged since the work's premiere in 1959 is the depth of Poulenc's personal identification. 'Elle, c'est moi,' he wrote while working on a score that he also described as an 'atrocious tragedy (my own)' – one written 'with the heart of a 20-year-old, alas, and the experience of a 60-year-old, double alas'. His affair with the still-anonymous and too-often-absent 'Louis' had been going through a bad patch. Duval was also in the midst of an emotional crisis, and they referred to the work as 'a chronicle of our torment'. It is this sense of deep identification that adds to the power of *La voix humaine*; it is not a piece you want to listen to very often.

Just to come down to earth, it is technically brilliant. Poulenc writes for a full orchestra, but uses it very sparingly, so the tuttis, when they come, and the purely lyrical moments amid the faultlessly composed *arioso* – what word setting! – hit you with the force of a pile-driver. It is, beyond dispute, a little masterpiece.

Poulenc • La voix humaine
Prom 30 Sunday 10 August, 7.30pm

HANDEL Saul

Lindsay Kemp tells how the Old Testament tale of the envy-maddened king inspired Handel to create the first great masterpiece of English oratorio

ABOVE
George Frideric Handel:
detail of the 1756 portrait
by Thomas Hudson (1701–79)

In January 1739 a London architect named William Kent wrote (if it can be called that) to a friend about a performance he had attended of *Saul*, a new English oratorio by the man acknowledged as the greatest composer of the age, George Frideric Handel:

'I was there with a handsom widow fatt, which has given much diversion to the looker on … There is a pritty concerto in the oratorio there is some stops in the Harpsicord that are little bells, I thought it had been some squerrls in a cage.'

If this was the level at which some of his audience listened in, Handel was ready and waiting. For his fifth English oratorio, the showman in him had brought in not only the 'little bells' (actually a keyboard-operated carillon), but also booked a hefty orchestra and borrowed two specially large kettle-drums from the Tower of London. He had also considered ending the piece with a 'Hallelujah' chorus. Clearly he was out to make a big noise with the public.

But of course Handel was much more than a showman. His interest in English oratorio may have originated a few years earlier as an opportunistic way of making money at times when Italian opera, his first love, was doing bad box office, but that was never going to prevent his genius from shining through. For the Handel scholar Winton Dean, *Saul* is 'one of the supreme masterpieces of dramatic art, comparable with the *Oresteia* and *King Lear*'; and, indeed, one senses that it was here that Handel first realised the full potential of the fledgling genre he himself had created. With works such as *Messiah*, *Samson* and *Jephtha* still ahead of him, this was his first great oratorio.

What makes it great are not the colourful orchestra and theatrical coups, for all that they add to the work's attractiveness. As so often with Handel, the heart of the work lies in the character portrayals, in the penetrating depictions of the inner self of which, as an opera-composer, he had already proved himself one of the finest masters. In Saul, the Old Testament warrior-king who suffers madness, ruin and death as a result of his jealousy of the young David, he found a character worthy of his talents and his compassion, one whose end he makes a noble and redeeming one despite his previous violent and irrational behaviour. In David he drew a talented youth whose stature grows until he is ready for kingship himself, so that in the moving final scene he can lead the public mourning not just for Saul but for the entire defeated Hebrew nation.

Here, too, Handel's skills in dramatically involved choral-writing are spectacularly displayed – the chorus really is the voice of the people – but elsewhere his ability to probe a particular moral predicament is also much in evidence, as when the great chorus 'Envy! eldest born of Hell!' holds the oratorio's central tenet in iron grip. This was something deep and new, and Handel must have known it. For him, oratorio had become the future.

TOP RIGHT
The Death of Saul (c1680)
by Johann Heinrich Schönfeld
(1609–84)

Handel • Saul
Prom 46 Sunday 24 August, 7.00pm

TCHAIKOVSKY Manfred

Anthony Holden reveals the guilty secret that lies behind the Russian composer's most personal yet least-performed symphony

'I have devoted a year of my life to this symphony,' wrote a shattered Tchaikovsky after completing his *Manfred* in the autumn of 1885. 'An inner voice tells me that I have not laboured in vain, that this will turn out to be perhaps the best of my symphonic works.' Within a few years, as was his temperamental wont, he disowned the piece, calling it 'abominable … I loathe it deeply.' Posterity has begged to differ.

The idea behind the work dated back 20 years, to Berlioz's last visit to Moscow in 1867, when he had conducted his *Harold in Italy*. Inspired by Byron's *Childe Harold*, the piece moved the critic Vladimir Stasov to draw up a programme for a symphony based on Byron's long poem *Manfred*; he offered it to Balakirev, who passed it on to Berlioz. The Frenchman was unimpressed, and there the matter rested until Balakirev resurfaced in Tchaikovsky's life after an absence of a decade.

It was the kindly if interfering Balakirev who, back in 1869, had handed the young Tchaikovsky the idea for a fantasy overture based on Shakespeare's *Romeo and Juliet*. The older composer's fortunes had subsequently declined as steadily as the younger one's had prospered, to the point where Balakirev had been forced to take a menial job and withdraw from musical life. So he was thrilled to receive a score of the revised *Romeo and Juliet* in 1880; typically, he replied to Tchaikovsky with 'the programme for another overture which you would do wonderfully well': *Manfred*, in the version shunned by Berlioz.

Then busy orchestrating his opera *Mazeppa*, Tchaikovsky too played hard to get, merely making polite noises before eventually re-reading Byron's poem in the Alps – where, of course, it is set – while visiting a dying friend. A reunion in Moscow with Balakirev, who was also helping him rediscover his religious faith, finally persuaded him to undertake the composition originally intended for Berlioz 18 years earlier.

Reworking Balakirev's revision of Stasov, Tchaikovsky devoted as much time, effort and soul-searching to *Manfred* as to any work he ever wrote. Coming eight years after his Fourth Symphony, and three years before his Fifth, it proved the perfect interim vehicle for his ceaseless angst about his sexuality – in this instance, as he saw it, his incestuous longings for his teenage nephew Vladimir ('Bob') Davidov.

If Byron was expiating his own love for his half-sister Augusta in Manfred's 'forbidden' longings, Tchaikovsky would now do the same in music. He anticipates Britten by fastening on a literary portrait of an outsider, rejected by a cruel and conventional world, and making it his own – not least with the hint in his B major ending that redemption followed his tragic hero's demise. Despite a triumphant premiere in Moscow, and continued success throughout his lifetime, the piece came to haunt him as a reminder of his own guilty secret. The most under-performed of his major works, Tchaikovsky's *Manfred* and its passionate agonies reveal as much about the man as about the composer.

Tchaikovsky • Manfred
Prom 52 Thursday 28 August, 7.30pm

LEFT
Manfred on the Jungfrau (1861) by Ford Madox Brown (1821–93)

BELOW
Pyotr Ilyich Tchaikovsky, painted in the last year of his life (1893) by Nikolai Kuznetsov (1850–1930)

THE LATE 'LATE JUNCTION' PROM

In the spirit of BBC Radio 3's boundary-breaking late-night series, a specially extended Late Night Prom encompasses a world of music – from Africa, the Caribbean, Scandinavia, the Balkans, Armenia and Latin America

Reflecting a landscape of extraordinary global musics that look resolutely forwards while also building on the traditions of age-old cultures, the Late 'Late Junction' Prom recreates live on stage the spirit of adventure that drives Radio 3's landmark week-night series.

The finger-popping, infectiously danceable big-band ska, reggae and blues beat of BBC Jazz Award-winners, the Jazz Jamaica All Stars, and the ebullient Balkan brass-wind-and-vocal pyrotechnics of Macedonia's Koçani Orkestar contrast with the gorgeous, intensely lyrical songs of the charismatic guitarist Manecas Costa, from the tiny African state of Guinea-Bissau, who will be joined by Venezuelan harpist Carlos Orozco.

Ellika and Solo – winners in the 'Boundary Crossing' category of the BBC Radio 3 Awards for World Music 2003 – demonstrate a rare transcontinental empathy, with Swedish-born Ellika's violin, deeply resonant of Nordic folk music, fusing seamlessly with mesmeric melodies from Solo's *kora* that speak directly from the heart of Mali.

Two stunning solo performers complete the global picture. From Finland, Kimmo Pohjonen brings a solo performance that is both sonically and theatrically riveting – the familiar accordion of folk tradition transported into a parallel universe, where electronic and acoustic sounds combine to speak a new and unique musical language; while Arto Tuncboyacian offers a veritable surprise package that creates a rare rapport with his audiences, using an unlikely array of percussion, voice and traditional stringed instruments from his native Armenia.

The Late 'Late Junction' Prom
Prom 21 Saturday 2 August, 10.00pm–2.00am

RIGHT (FROM TOP LEFT)
Macedonia's Koçani Orkestar;
Ellika and Solo, Radio 3 World
Music Award-winners from
Sweden and Mali; Manecas
Costa, charismatic guitarist;
Kimmo Pohjonen, Finnish
accordionist (and friends);
Armenia's Arto Tuncboyacian;
and BBC Jazz Award-winners,
the Jazz Jamaica All Stars

BBC SINGERS

Chief Conductor: Stephen Cleobury
Principal Guest Conductor: Bob Chilcott
Associate Composer: Edward Cowie
Conductor Fellows 2002/3: Justin Doyle & Aidan Oliver

BBC SINGERS

2003 CONCERTS INCLUDE APPEARANCES IN LONDON, OXFORD, NORWICH, CAMBRIDGE, HUDDERSFIELD, BUDAPEST, LJUBLJANA, ROTTERDAM, HAARLEM AND TONBRIDGE

Twenty-four of the best musicians in the world

Choir & Organ March 2003

The BBC Singers were superb

Daily Telegraph August 2002

Always conveying the truth of words and music

The Independent October 2002

Impressively agile and spot-on delivery of incredibly complex & virtuoso contemporary works

Der Landbote Zürich 12/11/02

For more information about forthcoming concerts, join the BBC Singers' free mailing list
Tel: 020 7765 1862 • Email: singers@bbc.co.uk • www.bbc.co.uk/singers

BBC RADIO 3 90-93 FM

GERALD PLACE

THE VOICE OF CLASSICAL MUSIC

3 ISSUES FOR JUST £1

Take advantage of our special offer to try 3 issues of Gramophone for just £1!
Gramophone is your insight into the world of classical music, with
all the latest news and views from the top of the classical world.

You won't need to take any further action to continue your subscription.
After the trial you will pay just £10.45 every 3 issues saving you 15% off the
shop price. All this plus free priority delivery *and* a free CD with every issue.

**TO SUBSCRIBE SIMPLY COMPLETE THE COUPON OR CALL OUR
HOTLINE ON 01795 414823** – Please have your bank details ready and quote BBCP3

GRAMOPHONE
THE CLASSICAL MUSIC MAGAZINE

SUBSCRIPTION ORDER FORM

☐ **Yes please send me the next 3 issues of Gramophone
for just £1. I understand that my subscription will
continue at the special rate of £10.45 every 3 issues
thereafter. If the magazine is not for me I can write
and cancel at any time during the trial period.**

YOUR DETAILS

BLOCK CAPITALS PLEASE (must be completed)

Mr/Mrs/Ms_____Initials_____Surname_____

Address_____

_____

_____

Postcode_____Telephone_____

e-mail_____

DIRECT DEBIT PAYMENT

Instructions to your Bank or Building Society to pay by Direct Debit

To: The Manager: Bank/Building Society

Address

Postcode

Name(s) of Account Holder(s)

DIRECT Debit

Originators ID No. 850699

Branch Sort Code   Bank/Building Society account number

Reference Number (for office use only)

Banks and Building Societies may not accept Direct Debit instructions for some types of account

Instruction to your Bank or Building Society Please pay Haymarket Publishing Services Ltd
Direct Debits from the account detailed in this instruction subject to the safeguards assured by the Direct Debit
Guarantee. I understand that this instruction may stay with Haymarket Publishing Services Ltd and, if so, details will be
passed electronically to my Bank/Building Society.

Signature(s)   Date

BBCP3

Terms and Conditions: This offer is open to UK subscribers only and is a direct debit
offer. Details of the Direct Debit Guarantee are available on request. If stock runs out
you will be given 3 free issues and then charged the advertised rate. Offer closes on
1st September 2003. Overseas rates are available by calling +44 (0) 1795 414826.

We may use your contact details to inform you about other offers and reputable companies, whose products
and services may be of interest to you. Please tick this box if you do not wish to receive such offers ☐

GLYNDEBOURNE
ON TOUR
2003

W A MOZART
Idomeneo
A new production by Peter Sellars,
premiered at the 2003 Festival

G VERDI
La traviata
Based on the original production,
directed by Sir Peter Hall

G F HANDEL
Theodora
A revival of Peter Sellars' production,
premiered in 1996

GLYNDEBOURNE	7 – 25 October
WOKING	28 October – 1 November
MILTON KEYNES	4 – 8 November
NORWICH	11 – 15 November
STOKE-ON-TRENT	18 – 22 November
PLYMOUTH	25 – 29 November
OXFORD	2 – 6 December
EDINBURGH	9 – 13 December

To join our FREE mailing list and receive full details
of the 2003 Tour please call 01273 815000
or email info@glyndebourne.com
or write to: GTO Mailing list, Freepost BR (235),
Glyndebourne, Lewes, East Sussex BN8 4BR

www.glyndebourne.com

'GLYNDEBOURNE ON TOUR
...A YOUTHFUL AND
VIBRANT JOURNEY'
SUNDAY INDEPENDENT 2000

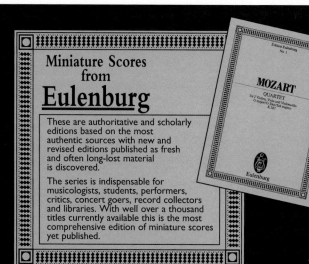

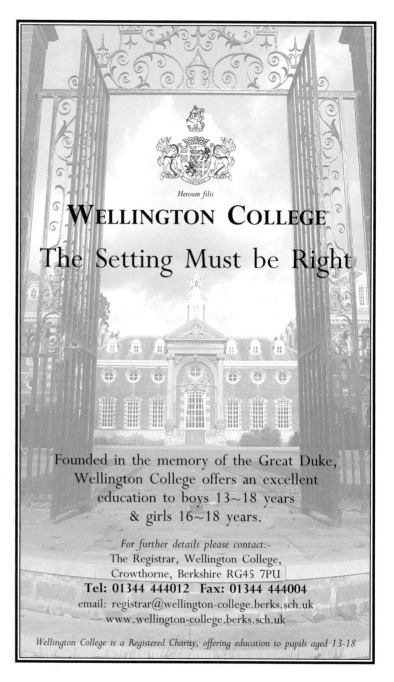

Tucked away in a little side street ....

behind 16th Century fortifications is probably one of the most acoustically perfect theatres in Europe. A small gem of the Baroque, the Manoel Theatre in Valletta bears the name of the Grand Master of the Order of St John who built it. Today the theatre is the stage for the annual Opera Festival in March and the biannual Baroque Festival in May, as well as a full programme of plays and concerts that make it one of the busiest in Europe.

The theatre complements the numerous ornate palazzos and majestic churches that make up Valletta, the capital city of Malta. Often described as a city built by gentlemen for gentlemen, Valletta is a UNESCO World Heritage Site and the cultural hub of the Mediterranean island. The cathedral and churches overflow with art, silver and marble; the palazzos hide sumptuous interiors behind discreetly elegant and imposing facades. Its fortifications no longer serve to defend it from invading marauders but stand as proud witness to the island's chequered past.

For thousands of years Malta has welcomed visitors from far and wide, visitors who have left their mark on the history, culture, art and architecture of the island. Malta lays claim to the oldest free-standing temples in the world alongside mysterious archaeological remains straight out of the pages of Greek mythology that, according to some, purport the island as the fabled Lost City of Atlantis.

An island of superlatives, Malta is an eclectic mix of cultures reflecting its diverse history. If you had to single out just one factor that makes the island unique, it is just that – it is Malta.

For further information www.visitmalta.com or call the Malta Tourist Office on 020 8877 6990. Further details on the Manoel Theatre on www.manoeltheatre.com.mt

NEW MUSIC

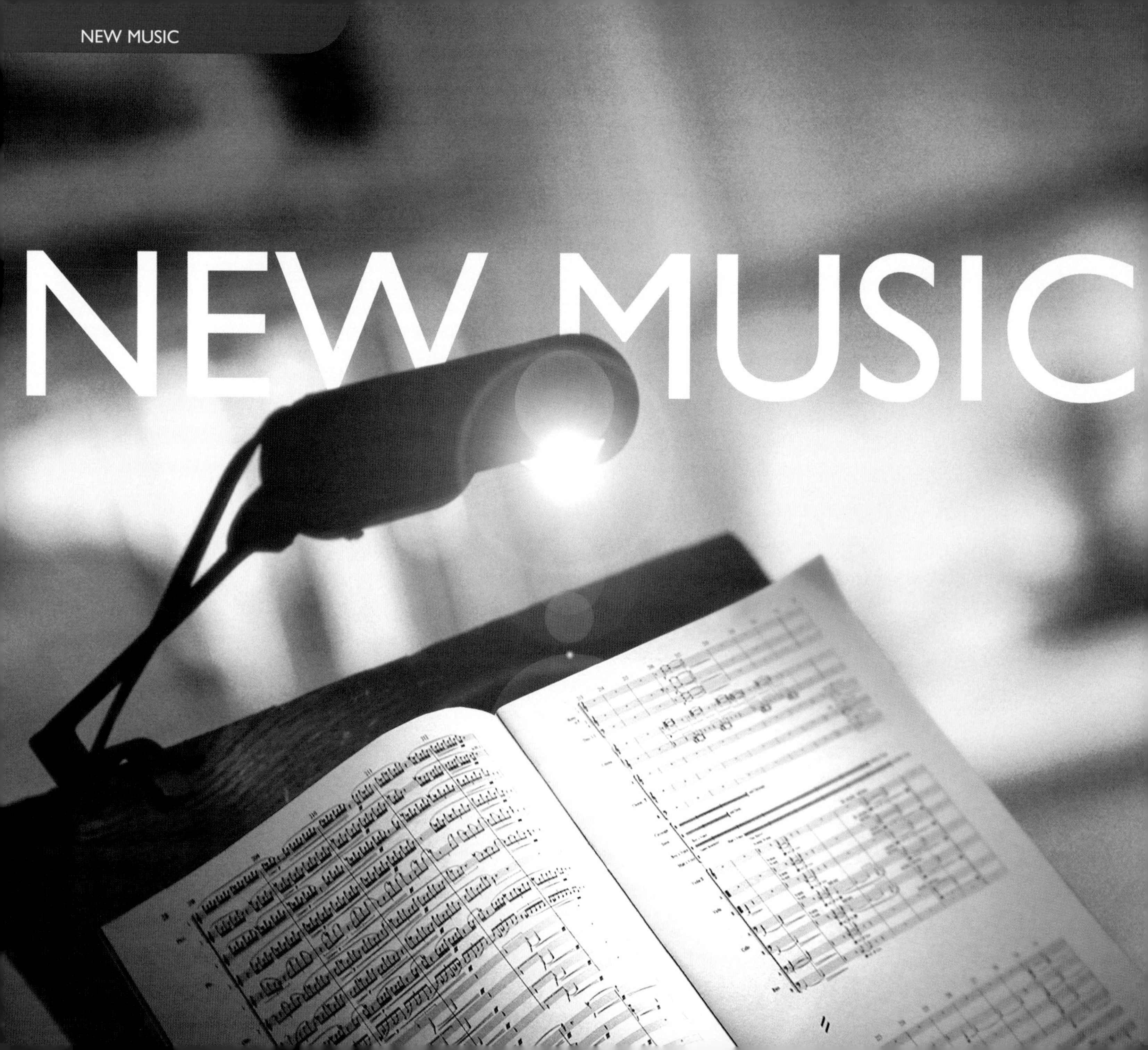

Proms commissions and premieres

With 28 new works by 26 composers from across the world, this year's Proms cover the full spectrum of contemporary writing. Ivan Hewett **sets the scene,** David Threasher **previews the pieces**

New music has always been a vital, colourful thread in the Proms tapestry. This season includes no fewer than 28 premieres by living composers, a dozen of them British, the rest from Estonia, Finland, China, Georgia, Germany, South Africa, Austria, Hungary and the USA. With a geographical spread that wide, you'd expect the pieces to show a huge variety of style and tone and aesthetic. But even within the British works, the range is pretty astonishing. It's a far cry from the typical Proms new-music roster of the Sixties or Seventies, when pieces could be confidently divided into two broad camps: the avant-garde and the conservative. What we have in this season – and it's a fair reflection of the state of new music in the wider world – is a plurality of pluralities, where the only trend seems to be the lack of any trends.

Well, almost. Once you've got over the first impression of bewildering variety, connections – some overt, some hidden – start to emerge. Despite all the predictions of the death of 'new old music', there's plenty of evidence that uncompromising modernism is still thriving. The tone might be muted and oblique, as in the violin concerto *en sourdine* by the 32-year-old German Matthias Pintscher (UK premiere, Prom 57), or slowly melancholy, as in Harrison Birtwistle's *The Shadow of Night* (UK premiere, Prom 72). Or it might be energetic and rapid-fire, as in Esa-Pekka Salonen's *Insomnia* (UK premiere, Prom 59), which takes a rather different view of things nocturnal, or Colin Matthews's *Vivo* (London premiere, Prom 12). The nocturnal theme reappears in Joseph Phibbs's new piece for the Last Night (Prom 73), though it's counterpointed by ideas of light and energy. It's a bold move, to programme a piece of rigorous abstraction for the Last Night of the Proms, though Phibbs swears he has no plans to 'cause a Panic', as Birtwistle famously did in 1995.

In several pieces a modernist stance goes hand-in-hand with antique subject-matter. Picking up on this year's theme of Greek myths, John Woolrich's new concerto for orchestra, *Double Mercury* (Prom 51), is inspired by both the silvery, liquid metal and the winged messenger of the gods. But there are other ancient sources of inspiration at work. Judith Weir's *The Welcome Arrival of Rain* (UK premiere, Prom 26) draws on a 1,000-year-old Hindu text, Kevin Volans's *Strip-Weave* (Prom 34) reconceives in musical terms the peculiar mixture of order and surprise you find in traditional North African weaving, while Chen Yi's Percussion Concerto (European premiere, Prom 41) mingles the clashing cymbals of Chinese opera with Western instruments.

Not all the cultural references in this year's premieres are exotic or ancient. Some are much closer to home. The Viennese-born HK Gruber's *Dancing in the Dark* (UK premiere, Prom 20) draws on the sounds of his native city, while in his new work for Sir Simon Rattle and the Berliner Philharmoniker, *Aus einem Tagebuch* (UK premiere, Prom 56), Heiner Goebbels quotes passages from his own music.

In seven of the premieres the allegiance to the Western tradition is declared through old-fashioned generic titles like 'concerto' and 'symphony'. There are two symphonies, one by James MacMillan – his Third, subtitled *Silence* (European premiere, Prom 9) – and one by the Finn Kalevi Aho – his Ninth (London premiere, Prom 40) – though the latter is also a disguised concerto, with a prominent solo part for trombone (doubling sackbut). There are also five 'straight' concertos, two of them for percussion – Chen Yi's (see above) and Joe Duddell's new BBC commission, *Ruby* (Prom 10); one for trumpet by Sally Beamish (London premiere, Prom 25); and two for violin, one by the Estonian composer Erkki-Sven Tüür (London premiere, Prom 19), the other by Oliver Knussen (London premiere, Prom 35). Of course, the mere use of the word 'concerto' needn't imply a traditional rhetoric, and in the case of Knussen's (described by him as a kind of high-wire act for the soloist) it definitely won't. Tüür's Concerto is likely to be unsettling in a different way; he dares to mix things that are usually taken to be mutually exclusive: straightforward diatonic harmony, cluster chords, murmuring 'textures' *à la* Ligeti, a sudden burst of minimalism. Like Aho and Tüür, the Georgian composer Giya Kancheli (*Warzone*, UK premiere, Prom 43) also tends to espouse an out-and-out, and once-unfashionable, romanticism.

If one overriding theme emerges from this bird's-eye view, it is that new music, even of a modernist sort, is now open to the world, no longer wrapped up in its own processes, no longer afraid to address big themes. So, for example, James MacMillan's new symphony tackles issues of belief and doubt while, in *On the Transmigration of Souls* (European premiere, Prom 13), John Adams dares to take on the biggest event of recent times – the tragedy of 9/11 – in a setting of heart-breakingly simple messages left by the bereaved for their missing loved ones at 'Ground Zero'.

'I knew immediately that I very much wanted to do this piece – in fact I *needed* to do it'

John Adams (b. 1947)

On the Transmigration of Souls

European premiere • Prom 13

When the New York Philharmonic approached John Adams about a work commemorating the first anniversary of the 9/11 atrocities in Manhattan, he didn't even need to think whether to say yes or no. 'I knew immediately that I very much wanted to do this piece – in fact I *needed* to do it. Being given the opportunity to make a work of art that would speak directly to people's emotions allowed me not only to come to grips personally with all that had happened, but also gave me a chance to give something to others.' The work combines Adams's trademark orchestral virtuosity with stark recordings of city noises and the names of those who died, and a chorus chanting messages written on the hastily prepared memorial placards that soon surrounded 'Ground Zero'. 'When we say "words fail" in situations like this, we mean it. So I realised that one of the great challenges of composing this piece would be finding a way to set the humblest of expressions like "He was the apple of my father's eye" or "She looks so full of life in that picture".'

Kalevi Aho (b. 1949)

Symphony No. 9

London premiere • Prom 40

Composed in 1994, Kalevi Aho's Ninth Symphony was originally going to be called *Sinfonia concertante* No. 2 – not a pure symphony, but not a full-blown concerto either. It was written for the extraordinary Swedish trombonist Christian Lindberg, who was last heard at the Proms in 2000 as the soloist in the UK premiere of Berio's *SOLO*, another of the many works he has commissioned. Aho's Ninth Symphony – a lighter conception than his Eighth, composed the previous year – mixes and matches music from the past and present, with sudden changes of style and 'time displacements', creating a sonic smorgasbord that jump-cuts from Aho's 'basic' style to a minuet here, flowing Romanticism there, neo-classicism *à la* Hindemith at one moment, pastiche Renaissance brass music at another. Not only is Lindberg required to display his athletic, multiphonic virtuosity, but he too joins in the time-travel, laying aside his modern trombone for a reproduction Baroque sackbut.

Sally Beamish (b. 1956)

Trumpet Concerto

London premiere • Prom 25

Sally Beamish's worklist is liberally sprinkled with concertos – for the violin of Anthony Marwood, the viola of Philip Dukes, the cello of Robert Cohen, the oboe of Douglas Boyd and the saxophone of John Harle. To these is now added a Trumpet Concerto, dedicated to Håkan Hardenberger. It's inspired partly by Italo Calvino's book *Invisible Cities* which, Beamish explains, 'reflects aspects of the organised architecture but seeming randomness of city life; sparkling though shabby beauty; spectacular skylines; in contrast to the dark, sordid underbelly – rusting pipes, waste, squalor.' She cites other influences too: 'the rich sound of jazz player Clifford Brown, the fact that my 12-year-old son Tom fills the house with the sound of trumpet for a few minutes each day (the theme of the first movement is taken from a piece I wrote for him when he was a baby), and of course Håkan himself, whose playing has inspired me ever since I played with the Academy of St Martin on his 1986 recording of the Haydn concerto.' And then there's the National Youth Orchestra of Scotland, which commissioned the piece. 'I'm a great fan of theirs. Their enthusiasm, energy and musicianship all played a part in my visualisation of the concerto.'

Sir Harrison Birtwistle (b. 1934)

The Shadow of Night

UK premiere • Prom 72

Albrecht Dürer's engraving *Melencolia I* – which depicts a dark-faced angel in a scene strewn with artefacts from an alchemist's workshop – first inspired Sir Harrison Birtwistle in his 1976 work of the same title, written for the clarinettist Alan Hacker and the Scottish National Orchestra. Commissioned over a quarter of a century later by the Cleveland Orchestra to write a new work, he turned once again to Dürer's symbol-laden image. *The Shadow of Night* extends the endlessly winding solo clarinet line of *Melencolia I*, building sinuous woodwind soliloquies over intricate polyphonic string patterns. Also present in the musical fabric are quotations from John Dowland's lute song 'In Darkness Let Me Dwell', a song in which Birtwistle found a musical symbol for the melancholy that imbues *The Shadow of Night*, which Christoph von Dohnányi, who conducted the Cleveland premiere, brings to the Proms with the Philharmonia Orchestra.

Elliott Carter (b. 1908)

Boston Concerto

European premiere • Prom 35

Now in his 95th year and showing no signs of slowing down, Elliott Carter is surely the grand old man of American music. One of two new pieces receiving their first performances this year, his *Boston Concerto* – premiered in April by Ingo Metzmacher and the Boston Symphony Orchestra, for whom it was composed – crosses the Atlantic to the Proms courtesy of Britain's big man of contemporary music, Oliver Knussen. Carter says of the work: 'The marvellous Boston Symphony was very important to me in the Twenties and Thirties as a Harvard student. At that time I went every Saturday and stood on the steps of Symphony Hall for a "rush seat" in the balcony. Those years also included singing in the Harvard Glee Club and with the BSO in great choral works. I am so grateful for those years and I have, I hope, written a "thank you" piece.' In the manner of a concerto for orchestra, each of the orchestra's sections is given its spell in the limelight, linked by what Carter describes as 'short orchestral *pizzicato* sections for the entire group, not unlike the plan of a *concerto grosso*'.

Philip Cashian (b. 1963)

Tableaux

World premiere • Prom 5

The music of Manchester-born Philip Cashian is new to the Proms, but he has developed an impressive list of works, including the orchestral *Nightmaze*, composed for a Japanese tour by the BBC National Orchestra of Wales, the recent *Io* and commissions from the London Symphony Orchestra, the Britten-Pears Orchestra, Sinfonia 21 and the Britten Sinfonia. *Tableaux* was commissioned for the Proms by Thomas Zehetmair and the Northern Sinfonia, after they had performed his Chamber Concerto last autumn. 'It's quite a fast, rhythmic piece,' says Cashian, 'in a single movement in three sections: a strong, muscular beginning; a quiet scherzo, shimmering with scintillating detail; then a two-part invention, with a processional element leading up to a big close. The challenge was to write fast contrapuntal music and keep the momentum going. I also wanted to write a piece that makes the orchestra sound larger than it is, so there's lots of trumpet and vibraphone, and little concertante groups breaking away from the orchestra.'

Chen Yi (b. 1953)

Percussion Concerto

European premiere • Prom 41

Evelyn Glennie – the doyenne of modern-day percussion virtuosos – has arguably done more than anyone else to expand the repertoire for percussion and orchestra. Chen Yi's Percussion Concerto was composed in 1998 for Glennie to perform with the Singapore Symphony Orchestra and, following a recent recording, she brings it to Europe for the first time at the Proms. Chen Yi was born in Guangzhou and studied in Beijing and New York; she now teaches at the University of Missouri in Kansas City, and her music is performed widely in North America and across South East Asia. Alongside the glockenspiels and xylophone that are the percussionist's stock in trade, the soloist in the Percussion Concerto also plays such instruments as the *dagu* (a large traditional Chinese drum) and the lithophone (a sort of stone xylophone), not to mention sundry Chinese opera gongs, temple blocks and Japanese cup bells. Not only will Evelyn Glennie negotiate all these, but the central movement also features her singing an ancient Chinese text.

Joe Duddell (b. 1972)

Ruby

BBC commission

World premiere • Prom 10

'There's nothing cool about being a classical composer,' says Joe Duddell – 'nothing at all.' But his burgeoning list of major premieres testifies to his growing reputation as one of the leading names of his generation. A former student of Steve Martland at the RAM, his *Parallel Lines* was commissioned by the BBC for Martland's band in 1999, and was followed the same year by *The Realside* for the BBC Singers. A Proms Chamber Music work, *Vaporize* for piano duet, in 2000 and his contribution to the King's Singers' *Oriana Collection* in last year's Proms led to the commission for this percussion concerto. Written for Duddell's long-time friend and collaborator, Colin Currie, it follows hard on the heels of another concertante percussion work, *Snowblind*, also composed for Currie, who toured it across Europe with the BT Scottish Ensemble last summer. The new work's title is, the composer confides, a private joke between Currie and himself.

Peter Eötvös (b. 1944)

Snatches of a Conversation

UK premiere • Prom 28

Renowned as a composer, conductor and advocate of new music, Peter Eötvös also has a reputation as one of the most original musical thinkers of his generation. A disciple of Boulez and Stockhausen, he combines in his music the rigour of the former with the compositional vigour of the latter to create works of sparkling sonority and conspicuous theatricality. Earlier works include *Korrespondenz*, in which a string quartet paraphrases fragments from Mozart's letters. *Snatches of a Conversation*, though, is the real thing. Commissioned for the Europäischer Musikmonat in Basle in 2001, not only does it feature a trumpet soloist playing a 'double bell' trumpet with a variety of mutes, but one member of the ensemble intones the eponymous (and carefully notated) snatches of the conversation. Described by Eötvös as 'mostly nonsense', they are filtered through an electronic 'noisemaker' that twists and deforms them still further, rendering them almost as half-heard snippets of a conversation not intended for our ears – a post-modern echo of Ligeti's *Aventures*, which Eötvös conducts later in the same concert.

Heiner Goebbels (b. 1952)

Aus einem Tagebuch

UK premiere • Prom 56

Heiner Goebbels's career has been one of experimentation and innovation: he has performed in groups such as the Sogenannten Linksradikalen Blasorchesters ('So-called Left Radical Wind Orchestra'), the experimental Duo Heiner Goebbels/ Alfred Harth and the rock group Cassiber. Jazz and rock musics have informed his compositions, as have an innate theatrical sense (his output is dominated by theatre and radio plays, which he directs himself) and an interest in noise. Collage and montage techniques are to the fore in many of his works, with various musical and non-musical objects superimposed upon each other. His newest work, *Aus einem Tagebuch* ('From a Diary'), is one such collage work: a prominent feature of the score – subtitled 'Kurze Eintragungen für Orchester' ('short entries for orchestra') – is a sample-list, with each sample dated (ranging from 09/1992 to 01/2003). The samples are from his earlier compositions, and are played from a keyboard, overlaid onto the orchestral foundation.

HK Gruber (b. 1943)

Dancing in the Dark

UK premiere • Prom 20

Vienna-born and bred (and a descendant of the Gruber who wrote 'Silent Night'), HK Gruber – known to all as 'Nali' – was a member of the Vienna Boys' Choir and studied at the city's Hochschule für Musik. The Austrian capital is a continuing presence in his music as well – in works such as his 'Austrian journal for orchestra' *Charivari*, based on Johann Strauss's *Perpetuum mobile*, and *Bring me the Head of Amadeus*, the soundtrack to a Mozart bicentenary film. His scores often include characteristically quirky extras, such as the cowhorn the soloist has to play in his trumpet concerto *Aerial* (premiered at the 1999 Proms), or the 'chansonnier' part he wrote for himself to sing in his 'pan-demonium' *Frankenstein!!*. Composed for the Vienna Philharmonic and Sir Simon Rattle, *Dancing in the Dark* continues the Viennese theme of Gruber's music, mixing the heady sound-world of Mahler's and Berg's Vienna with a 'funereal foxtrot', jazz and step-dance rhythms 'with Fred Astaire as their godfather'.

Giya Kancheli (b. 1935)

Warzone

UK premiere • Prom 43

Kancheli composed this work in tribute to Valery Gergiev, for the 2002 Rotterdam Gergiev Festival in advance of the Ossetian-born conductor's 50th birthday. Kancheli explains the title: 'I chose the Ossetian word *vorzon*, which means "love". But when I wrote this word in Latin characters it suddenly became clear to me that the sound of the word in a certain way corresponded to the English word "warzone". And indeed, in this transcription the word reflects what is happening in the world. As we know, it often takes just one thoughtless move to turn love into a "warzone". The way from "warzone" back to love, however, is long and hard.' Kancheli's music, which includes seven symphonies and numerous other orchestral works, has attracted epithets such as individual, beautiful, fragile, haunting; 'In my music, as in life,' he says, 'joy and sorrow are close to each other. Usually in my music grief and sorrow are stronger than joy. But in this piece it is joy that prevails!'

Oliver Knussen (b. 1952)

Violin Concerto

London premiere • Prom 35

'My ideal listener is someone who knows bugger all about new music but is not hostile, and is prepared to be taken by the hand and surprised.' So says Oliver Knussen, whose 50th birthday last year was celebrated with a Proms pairing of his scintillating Sendak operas *Where the Wild Things Are* and *Higglety Pigglety Pop!*. His Violin Concerto was commissioned by the Pittsburgh and Philadelphia orchestras, and premiered in Pittsburgh in April 2002. The soloist was Pinchas Zukerman, whom Knussen calls 'a much-appreciated (by me) supporter of my work – he conducted the US premiere of *Wild Things* in 1985, and asked me to write him something longer ago than either of us probably cares to remember'. The concerto is in three classically-titled movements – Recitative, Aria, Gigue – but 'despite the classical associations the expressive world is sometimes wildly at odds with expectations thus suggested, or so it seems to me. At times the violinist resembles a tightrope-walker progressing along a (decidedly unstable) high wire strung across the span that separates the opening and closing sounds of the piece.'

'My ideal listener is someone who knows bugger all about new music but is not hostile, and is prepared to be taken by the hand and surprised'

Malcolm Crowthers (Gruber, Knussen) Sikorski (Kancheli)

James MacMillan (b. 1959)

Symphony No. 3, 'Silence'

BBC/NHK co-commission

European premiere • Prom 9

Colin Matthews (b. 1946)

Vivo

London premiere • Prom 12

'It seems terribly important to me that we examine the spirituality of "one" in our immediate times, times in which we seem to be morally drowning in a political sea of aggression, greed and cultural intolerance'

Libby Larsen (b. 1950)

I It Am

BBC/Bach Choir co-commission

World premiere • Prom 16

For its first visit to the Proms, the Pennsylvania-based Bach Choir of Bethlehem – the oldest Bach Choir in the USA – felt it was a natural choice to ask Libby Larsen to compose a new work for them. 'It appealed to us to have an American composer write the new work, someone who knew our traditions and valued the place of the Bach Choir in American musical history,' says Greg Funfgeld, the Bach Choir's conductor. *I It Am* draws its text from the writings of Julian of Norwich and, says Larsen, 'suggests an exploration of the concept of Unity – one is all, all is one, and one is all that exists. It seems terribly important to me that we examine the spirituality of "one" in our immediate times, times in which we seem to be morally drowning in a political sea of aggression, greed and cultural intolerance. The cantata is an exposition of human experience revealed to us through these writings – that within each person light is dark and dark is light.'

Commissioned to compose a work for Tokyo's NHK Symphony Orchestra, James MacMillan found himself searching for a rapprochement between Eastern and Western cultural and musical divides. He found his answer in the work of the Japanese writer Shusaku Endo, like MacMillan a Catholic. Endo's *Silence* tells of the Job-like testing of a priest who witnesses the persecution of Christians in 17th-century Japan. Questioning his faith, he is challenged by God with silence, only reaching true understanding of his inner turmoil when he is finally provoked to surrender his faith and he tramples on an image of Christ. MacMillan has taken Endo's metaphor of silence as presence rather than absence, and fashioned a 35-minute symphony, whose music evolves from silence and returns to silence. His use of microtones is another nod towards the East, recalling the sound-world of the shakuhachi, the ancient Japanese notched flute.

Colin Matthews is known as an architect of large-scale musical forms, but has mostly been represented at recent Proms by shorter works: in 2000 he offered a tantalising glimpse of Pluto in his appendix to Holst's *The Planets*; a year later he provided a fanfare as a prelude to his orchestration of Britten's *Paul Bunyan* overture; and last year he was the prime mover in the collaborative *Bright Cecilia* variations, composed to mark the 10th birthday of *BBC Music Magazine*. Once again this season he is represented by a short work, *Vivo*, composed last year as a curtain-raiser for the Hallé, of which he is Associate Composer. Matthews says of the piece: '*Vivo* means "lively", which applies to just over half the work. There's a clear division into two parts, the second of which radically slows down the musical material tossed around rather frenetically in the first part, before the fast music returns at the end. The piece is dedicated to my wife, who often complains that I tend to end works softly, although not in this case.'

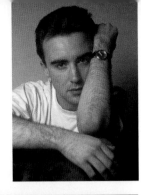

Mark O'Connor (b. 1962)

Violin Concerto No. 6, 'Old Brass'

World premiere • Prom 32

Described by the *New York Times* as 'complex, sophisticated early-21st-century classical music, reaching deeply into the refined, then the vernacular, and then knocking them dead with the brown-dirt whine of a Texas fiddle', Mark O'Connor's music is a unique blend of the traditions he has absorbed: the rich American aural folk tradition of the Texan fiddler Benny Thomasson, the French swing of Stephane Grappelli and the abundant melodies of 18th-century American composers. His Sixth Violin Concerto was inspired by a visit to a South Carolina plantation designed by Frank Lloyd Wright. O'Connor explains: 'Old Brass is a "southern" term relating to a person of both African and Native American heritage. Wright named his plantation "Auld Brass". And there is something I appreciate in Wright's vision as well. I have always embraced the philosophy that once a person impacts their creativity with the natural circumstances which surround them, then there is potential for that art to interface more naturally into the world.'

Joseph Phibbs (b. 1974)

New work

BBC commission

World premiere • Prom 73

'I am delighted to have been asked to write a piece for this year's Last Night – it's a unique chance to communicate to a large and extremely diverse audience within a magnificent setting.' Thus Joseph Phibbs on his most auspicious commission to date. He's worked with the BBC Symphony Orchestra before: his victory in the 1996 BBC Young Composers Forum resulted in a BBC SO commission to write *Soirée*, and more recently he composed *In Camera*, premiered under Leonard Slatkin in Macau before being heard in the orchestra's Barbican series. Now, with this Last Night commission, Phibbs, still in his late 20s, follows in the footsteps of his teacher at King's College, London – Sir Harrison Birtwistle, whose *Panic* was a memorable premiere in 1995. 'I'm hoping,' says Phibbs, 'to write a piece that brings together the various strands that make up what is most important to me as a composer from an expressive point of view, and to do this in the clearest and most direct way possible, without losing sight of the wonderful possibilities for adventure and virtuosity that are opened up when writing for an orchestra such as the BBC SO.'

Matthias Pintscher (b. 1971)

en sourdine

UK premiere • Prom 57

Still only in his early 30s, Matthias Pintscher made a name for himself very early in his career as a composer and conductor – he conducted the premiere of his ballet *Gesprungene Glocken* at the Berlin Staatsoper at the age of just 23, and has gone on to complete an opera, *Thomas Chatterton*, and numerous orchestral and chamber works. Many of his works take ideas from the visual arts and poetry: 'My music places its trust in the power of the poetic. I view it as an "imaginary theatre" full of mysteries and secrets, always rediscovering and redefining its own sensibility. It brings forth soundscapes into which the listener can plunge, unleashing vivid pictorial associations and turning into a mirror-image of faded realities.' A violin concerto in all but name, *en sourdine* was premiered in February by Frank Peter Zimmermann with the Berlin Philharmonic Orchestra under another composer-conductor featured in this year's Proms, Peter Eötvös.

Esa-Pekka Salonen (b. 1958)

Insomnia

UK premiere • Prom 59

Although best known to a wider audience as a conductor – he's been Music Director of the Los Angeles Philharmonic since 1992 – Esa-Pekka Salonen considers himself first and foremost a composer. Originally a card-carrying member of the Finnish avant-garde, he reached a turning-point in 1996 with his *L. A. Variations*; written for his West Coast players after a complete reconsideration of his individual sound-world, it pointed the way to a new virtuosity in his handling of the orchestra. *Insomnia* moves away from the steely brilliance of his tone poem *Giro* and the exhilaratingly loud *Foreign Bodies*, both heard at the Proms in recent years. 'Its sound is darker and deeper than my other recent orchestral works,' says Salonen. 'From early in the composition process I realised that this music was somehow about the night, but not in an idyllic, nocturnal way. I was more drawn towards the demonic, "dark" aspects of the night: the kind of persistent, compulsive thoughts that run through one's mind when lying hopelessly awake in the early hours.'

Robert Saxton (b. 1953)
Five Motets
BBC commission
World premiere • Prom 62
Sonata for Solo Cello on a Theme of Sir William Walton
London premiere • PCM 7

'The motets follow themes of hope, returns and wanderings, and are a sort of spin-off from the opera I've been working on, *The Wandering Jew*'

Robert Saxton's new set of motets was commissioned by the Clerks' Group to be interspersed among the movements of Josquin's *Missa Fortuna desperata*. 'The motets follow themes of hope, returns and wanderings,' says Saxton, 'and are a sort of spin-off from the opera I've been working on, *The Wandering Jew*.' Opening spaciously and building towards a closing triad, the outer motets, setting passages from Genesis in Latin, concern journeys made by Abraham and Jacob; the second and fourth motets set Saxton's own commentaries upon these journeys; while the central motet – 'a sort of scherzo, a choral dance' – sets the Israelites' song of deliverance from the book of Exodus. Another Saxton work, *Sonata for Solo Cello on a Theme of Sir William Walton*, is brought to London by Steven Isserlis, who premiered it at the Aldeburgh Festival in 2000. Walton labelled his theme 'Tema con variazioni' but never added the variations; Saxton's work is 'a voyage of discovery in search of Walton's melody'.

Erkki-Sven Tüür (b. 1959)
Violin Concerto
London premiere • Prom 19

Erkki-Sven Tüür is one of a new school of Baltic composers who have followed such figures as Arvo Pärt into the international limelight since the fall of Communism. Born in Estonia, he absorbed the classical music his father listened to, before becoming involved in Estonia's progressive rock scene during the 1970s. In the 1980s he turned to composition full time, creating a blend of diatonic harmony, serial techniques, minimalism, the tintinnabulations of Pärt and the aleatory methods of Lutoslawski. He says, 'My work as a composer is entirely concerned with the relation between emotional and intellectual energy; my pieces are abstract dramas in sound, with characters and a dynamic chain of events. In writing the Violin Concerto I considered as essential the changing relationship between the solo instrument and the surrounding sound landscape. The tensions, which come from the changes in this relationship, served as the motivation for the whole work. The Concerto is dedicated to my father, thanks to whom I was able to study music as a child.'

Kevin Volans (b. 1949)
Strip-Weave
World premiere of revised version • Prom 34

Kevin Volans came to prominence as the composer of *White Man Sleeps*, a set of five African dances made famous in an arrangement for the Kronos Quartet. Since that success, the Pietermaritzburg-born composer has moved on from the African models that informed his early work, developing a unique style that incorporates the unique timelessness of African traditions without resorting to pastiche.

Recent works have drawn upon minimalist art and architecture as a source of inspiration, invoking the Japanese term 'wabi' ('emptiness'), stripping music of its content. Now resident in Ireland, Volans wrote *Strip-Weave* to launch the Ulster Orchestra's 2002 autumn season in Belfast. The title refers to a North African cloth, woven in narrow patterned strips that are then sewn together to form new patterns, sometimes regular and sometimes unpredictable. The patterns are depicted by three spatially separated groups of wind and brass, while the larger fabric is provided by strings and percussion.

Judith Weir (b. 1954)

The Welcome Arrival of Rain
UK premiere • Prom 26
The Voice of Desire
BBC commission
World premiere • PCM 4

Commissioned by the Minnesota Orchestra for its centenary, Judith Weir's *The Welcome Arrival of Rain* was premiered in January under Osmo Vänskä, whose successor as Chief Conductor of the BBC Scottish Symphony Orchestra, Ilan Volkov, will direct its UK premiere at the Proms. The inspiration for the work comes from an 18,000-verse Hindu text, the *Bhagavata Purana*, composed about 900AD, and an illustration of the text that Weir saw in the Philadelphia Museum of Art. Weir describes the piece as 'an orchestral work celebrating nature's exuberance and fertility as experienced in the eagerly-awaited arrival of India's monsoon rains'. Her new song-cycle *The Voice of Desire* – setting texts by Bridges, Keats and Hardy, along with traditional Yoruba poetry – was specially commissioned for this year's Proms Chamber Music series and for the mezzo-soprano Alice Coote, a Radio 3 New Generation Artist.

James Wood (b. 1953)

Tongues of Fire
World premiere • Prom 67

For James Wood – composer, conductor, percussionist and creator and discoverer of new instruments – rhythm is a primary concern. Commissioned to write a work for the 140th anniversary of the Yale Glee Club, he was struck by the choir's 'clean, punchy singing; it gave me the courage to enjoy the more intricate side of my rhythmic techniques, much as I have always done in my "pan-percussion music".' But the new piece is also very different from most of his other music. 'It is wild, joyous and extremely upbeat – even, dare I say it, verging on the post-modern (as a modernist, I abhor this notion!).' The central text of *Tongues of Fire* is from the Acts of the Apostles, sung in Latin-American Spanish, which Wood chose for 'its crisp rhythmic articulations and possibilities for Salsa-like syncopations'. The accompaniment is built around a quartet of oil drums: 'I was astonished by the almost orchestral richness of these apparently crude instruments. I went on to discover even greater potential in their use as resonators for other instruments. Nor is their association with fire a coincidence.'

John Woolrich (b. 1954)

Double Mercury
BBC/Britten Sinfonia co-commission
World premiere • Prom 51

'*Double Mercury* takes its inspiration from Ovid and is about transformation and metamorphosis,' says John Woolrich of his latest work. And transformation and metamorphosis are continuing preoccupations in his music: he recomposed a Monteverdi aria for *Ulysses Awakes* and built *The Theatre Represents a Garden: Night* from fragments of Mozart, while *Arcangelo*, composed for the Academy of Ancient Music and premiered in March, is based on music by Corelli. The past decade has seen an impressive flow of orchestral music from Woolrich's pen, including concertos for viola and cello, and the large-scale Oboe Concerto, a 1996 Proms commission. Of this year's new work, though, he says, 'The title refers to the two meanings of "mercury": Mercury the god who changes from old to young, and the element mercury which is used as an agent in chemical changes.'

'The title refers to the two meanings of "mercury": Mercury the god who changes from old to young, and the element mercury which is used as an agent in chemical changes'

Malcolm Crowthers (Weir, Wood, Woolrich)

BBC Symphony Chorus 75

75th Anniversary Season

Director Stephen Jackson

Alex von Koettlitz

This season the BBC Symphony Chorus celebrates its 75th anniversary with a number of concerts highlighting its very special talents.

BBC Proms 2003
Featuring in five concerts with **Prokofiev's** *Ivan the Terrible* on the First Night and the UK premiere of **John Adams's** *On the Transmigration of Souls*, as well as the famous Last Night.

BBC Symphony Orchestra Barbican Season 2003-2004
Highlights include:
Honegger *Le Roi David*
Berlioz *L'enfance du Christ*, in Westminster Cathedral
Bartók *Cantata Profana*
Shostakovich Symphony No 13

'a blazing performance… with the BBC Symphony Chorus in glorious voice in its 75th anniversary year.'
The Times

The BBC Symphony Chorus would like to hear from potential new members. If you enjoy making music at the highest level with great conductors and orchestras, then this is the choir for you.

To find out more, contact Graham Wood, Chorus Administrator, or visit our website.

BBC Maida Vale Studios
Delaware Road
London W9 2LG
Tel: 020 7765 4715
Fax: 020 7286 3251
e-mail: graham.wood@bbc.co.uk

www.bbc.co.uk/orchestras/so/chorus

BBC SCOTTISH SYMPHONY ORCHESTRA

Ilan Volkov Chief Conductor

"Volkov has one of Britain's finest orchestras at his disposal… Here was a young conductor intoxicated with the score, and playing his orchestra for all it was worth. Volkov was heady in his engagement with the music's rhythmic power and searing instrumental confrontations."
HILARY FINCH, THE TIMES

"…he has all the makings of one of the really great conductors. Seek him out. Watch him in action. Hear the results; if you have a soul, you will be blown away."
MICHAEL TUMELTY, THE HERALD

"Volkov held his players and his audience in musical limbo for what seemed like minutes: testament to the strength of his relationship with the orchestra, and his natural, unaffected charisma."
TOM SERVICE, THE GUARDIAN

BBC SSO Season Highlights

- 2003/2004 Festival appearances in China, Edinburgh, St Magnus, Prague, Estonia
- BBC Young Musician 2004 finals
- Berlioz Day: including the complete *Romeo and Juliet* and *Symphonie Fantastique*
- Concert performances of *Elektra*, *Lohengrin* and *Bluebeard's Castle*

BBC RADIO 3 90-93FM

www.bbc.co.uk/bbcsso

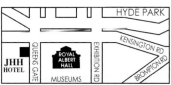

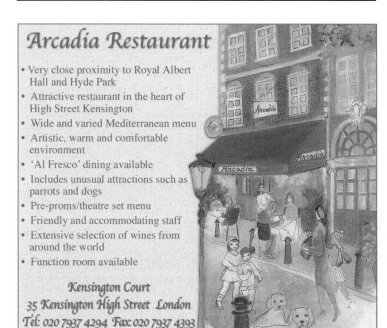

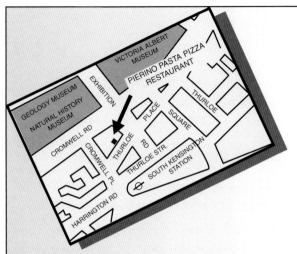

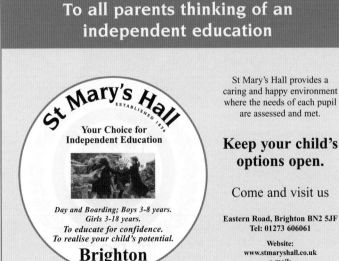

ARTISTS

Leading from the front

One of the many attractions of any Proms season, writes Sue Knussen, **is the chance to hear visiting conductors and orchestras from abroad whose work most of us know only through recordings or broadcasts**

Legends of the great conductors abound. Luckily, the performances – and the behaviour – of many of the most famous 20th-century maestros have been documented in recordings and on film. No-one who has ever heard them can forget the terrifying effect of the angry outbursts captured in some of the rehearsal recordings of Arturo Toscanini, or the slightly pompous but undoubtedly charismatic gestures seen in filmed examples of Leopold Stokowski at work. But, as with all great conductors, their sheer force of personality seems to have coloured the sound their orchestras made.

Today's orchestras would certainly not tolerate some of the more dictatorial behaviour of those earlier maestros. Yet, however mysteriously they achieve it, there's no doubting the unique effect individual conductors still have on the orchestras before whom they stand. This season's visitors include some of the most eminent musicians working with orchestras today, and the variety of techniques and personalities, of stylistic approaches and interpretations, that they will bring promises a summer of rich and rewarding musical contrasts.

Roger Norrington's revolutionary 1989 recording of Berlioz's *Symphonie fantastique* broke new ground in pioneering the period-aware performance of Romantic repertoire from Weber to Wagner

Sir Roger Norrington   Prom 39

SWR Stuttgart Radio
Symphony Orchestra

Growing out of the extraordinary 'Experience' weekends that, during the 1980s, he and his authentic-instrument orchestra, the London Classical Players, regularly devoted to the music of a single composer, setting the works in the context of the cultures and times in which they were written, Roger Norrington's revolutionary 1989 recording of Berlioz's *Symphonie fantastique* broke new ground in pioneering the period-style performance of Romantic repertoire from Weber to Wagner. It's appropriate therefore that, in this Berlioz bicentenary year, it is with the composer's neglected early opera *Benvenuto Cellini* that Norrington should be returning to the Proms with the German orchestra of which he has been Chief Conductor since 1998.

Though he is to be found more often in front of modern-instrument orchestras than period ones these days, Norrington continues to make musical waves. Only this year he wrote an article for the *New York Times* suggesting that the string sections of the world's symphony orchestras should abandon their habitual use of vibrato. 'The reason to do so,' he wrote, 'is not because pure tone is "authentic" but because it is beautiful, expressive and exciting' – three adjectives that perfectly describe an ideal Norrington performance.

Valery Gergiev Proms 42 & 43

Rotterdam Philharmonic Orchestra

Any Proms appearance by the Russian conductor Valery Gergiev is a cause for excitement, as his ambitious weekend of concerts with his Kirov Orchestra last year – encompassing a complete *Boris Godunov*, a Gubaidulina choral premiere and a pair of concert works by Prokofiev and Shostakovich – confirmed. While his career is truly international, spanning St Petersburg, where he is Artistic Director of the Mariinsky Theatre, and New York, where he is Principal Guest Conductor at the Metropolitan Opera, anyone thinking in strictly national stereotypes might be surprised to find that this fiery, passionate Russian is also closely associated with a Dutch orchestra, the Rotterdam Philharmonic, of which he has been Chief Conductor since 1995.

This year marks both Gergiev's 50th birthday and his 25th year at the Mariinsky Theatre. Having grown up in the then USSR, where he studied conducting with the legendary Ilya Musin, he can never have imagined that he would now be leading the life of an international jet-setter. And his repertoire is now equally cosmopolitan: his two Proms this year include works by Berlioz, Beethoven and Ravel as well as the perhaps more predictable Prokofiev and Kancheli.

Mariss Jansons Proms 53 & 54

Pittsburgh Symphony Orchestra

Another conductor from the former Soviet Union, Latvian-born Mariss Jansons is bringing his American orchestra to this season's Proms. The son of conductor Arvid Jansons, Mariss has been steeped in music from the start: his training and early career included contact with several of the great conducting teachers and conductors of the 20th century, including Hans Swarowsky, Herbert von Karajan and Yevgeny Mravinsky.

During his professional career, Jansons has conducted most of the world's major orchestras, gaining the respect of audiences and players alike for his extraordinary musical integrity and talent. There can be no stronger proof of his standing than his recent appointment as the next Chief Conductor of the Royal Concertgebouw Orchestra in Amsterdam, starting in September 2004. In the meantime, he takes up another Chief Conductorship this September at the Bavarian Radio Symphony Orchestra in Munich. These new appointments will, of course, coincide with the end of his highly successful tenure with the Pittsburgh Symphony Orchestra. So this summer's Proms appearances will be London's last chance to hear Jansons as the orchestra's Music Director.

Sir Simon Rattle Proms 55 & 56

Berliner Philharmoniker

Music-lovers would have to be living on another planet not to be aware that the past season saw Sir Simon Rattle's debut as Chief Conductor of the Berlin Philharmonic (or Berliner Philharmoniker, as we must now get used to calling them). Rattle has long been known for his commitment to contemporary music, as well as his interest in reassessing approaches to the performance of 18th- and 19th-century works, not to mention a deep affinity for Mahler and much of the music of the first half of the 20th century. He now has his dream instrument – a major-league orchestra rooted in the Classical and Romantic tradition but one that also embraces the opportunity to explore the music of today. Hence the presence in their two Proms of scores by György Ligeti and Heiner Goebbels alongside more familiar works by Bartók, Stravinsky, Brahms and Strauss.

Like so many other cities in the West, Berlin is facing economic challenges and cultural changes unimaginable 20 years ago. Typically, Rattle is embracing the challenge by helping his orchestra to adapt artistically to the times while retaining its strong relationship to the tradition it has developed. A vociferous advocate for education and orchestras' responsibilities towards it, he has initiated an educational component to the Berlin players' work that had not previously been there. Communication, after all – and communicating his passion for music, above all – is what a Simon Rattle performance is all about.

> Communication, after all –
> and communicating his
> passion for music, above
> all – is what a Simon Rattle
> performance is all about

Malcolm Crowthers (Gergiev), Steve J. Sherman (Jansons), Simon Fowler (Rattle)

Christoph Eschenbach Prom 59

NDR Symphony Orchestra, Hamburg

Christoph Eschenbach first made his name as one of the leading pianists of his generation, playing sublime Mozart as well as a wide range of other music in the major musical capitals of the world. He still plays the piano from time to time, but it is conducting that now receives the lion's share of his creative energy. He has held music directorships with a number of orchestras, including the Houston Symphony, of which he was appointed Conductor Laureate in 1999 after an 11-year tenure as its Music Director; the Orchestre de Paris, of which he has been Music Director since 2000; and the Ravinia Festival (the summer series of the Chicago Symphony Orchestra), of which he has been Music Director since 1994.

This September he also begins a new tenure as Music Director of the Philadelphia Orchestra. But it is the NDR SO, the Hamburg radio band of which he has been Chief Conductor since 1998, that he brings to this year's Proms.

As well as his deep affinity with the standard orchestral repertoire, Eschenbach has a strong commitment to the music of today, regularly programming new works such as the Esa-Pekka Salonen piece, *Insomnia*, whose UK premiere prefaces music by Beethoven and Brahms in the NDR SO's Prom.

Eschenbach's interests make him an ideal partner for the Hamburg orchestra, which has enjoyed a continuing history of collaboration with living composers and their champions ever since it was founded by the conductor Hans Schmidt-Isserstedt in the ruins of post-war Germany in 1945, when it was hailed in the American press as 'the old world's youngest major orchestra'.

> One cellist in a major US symphony orchestra who recently played alongside McFerrin reported that the experience had changed his whole approach to Baroque music and to music-making in general

Bobby McFerrin Prom 64

Vienna Philharmonic Orchestra

One of the most intriguing pairings in this year's Proms is the collaboration between the Vienna Philharmonic, the archetypal European orchestra, and American conductor-singer Bobby McFerrin. McFerrin is better known in the UK for his creative music-making in the jazz and pop worlds, achieving wide recognition in the 1980s with his No. 1 hit 'Don't Worry, Be Happy', while his 1988 'Thinking About Your Body' was cleverly co-opted for a TV ad for a well-known chocolate bar. But McFerrin, a truly extraordinary musician with roots in the classical world (his parents were both opera singers) as well as jazz and pop, has been developing a parallel career as a conductor for two decades now, studying with Leonard Bernstein and Seiji Ozawa among others. And sometimes, thanks to his four-octave range and dazzling array of vocal techniques, he combines conducting with singing, as he will be doing in his Proms debut concert, vocalising one of the two solo parts in a Vivaldi concerto for two cellos. One cellist in a major US symphony orchestra who recently played the other part alongside McFerrin reported that the experience had changed his whole approach to Baroque music and to music-making in general. It should be fascinating to hear the outcome of this collaboration between such an innovative New World artist and an orchestra so strongly rooted in Old World traditions.

A conductor who clearly believes in long-term musical relationships, Mehta typically elicits performances of great verve and panache. The close bond he shares with his Israeli orchestra will surely produce memorable music-making at the Royal Albert Hall

Zubin Mehta Prom 68

Israel Philharmonic Orchestra

Bombay-born Zubin Mehta comes from a musical family. His father, Mehli Mehta, was also a conductor and worked until the age of 90, when he retired as Music Director of a training orchestra for young musicians in Los Angeles, where Zubin was Music Director of the Philharmonic from 1962 to 1978, before moving on to the New York Philharmonic. He is currently Music Director of the Bavarian State Opera and conducts in many of the world's major opera houses as well as concert halls.

But his longest-standing relationship is with the orchestra with which he will appear at this summer's Proms – the Israel Philharmonic. Mehta's formal relationship with the orchestra began in 1969, when he was appointed Music Adviser, before becoming Music Director in 1977 and, in 1981, Music Director for Life. A conductor who clearly believes in long-term musical relationships, Mehta typically elicits performances of great verve and panache. The close bond he shares with his Israeli orchestra will surely produce memorable music-making at the Royal Albert Hall.

David Zinman Prom 71

Tonhalle Orchestra, Zürich

In the catalogues of recorded music, complete cycles of the Beethoven symphonies abound, and it is sometimes tempting to question the need for yet another. However, 1999 saw the release of one Beethoven cycle that produced a genuine buzz in the listening world, and not just because the new cycle from the Zürich-based Tonhalle Orchestra, under its American-born conductor David Zinman, was the first to use Jonathan Del Mar's new critical edition of the scores.

Zinman, who has been Music Director of Switzerland's oldest orchestra since 1995, is a long-time champion of new music and of American composers in particular. Also dedicated to the education of young musicians, he has been Music Director of the Aspen Music Festival and School since 1998, spending his summers mentoring gifted young musicians from around the world in the Rocky Mountain town otherwise best known as an up-market ski resort.

Zinman and his Tonhalle Orchestra have recently embarked upon a complete recorded edition of the orchestral works of Richard Strauss, whose *Don Juan* opens their Proms programme.

Conductors making their Proms debuts this season

Thomas Zehetmair Prom 5

Northern Sinfonia

Already familiar to Proms audiences as an exceptional violinist, the Salzburg-born musician makes his Proms conducting debut with the orchestra of which he became Music Director last September, and which he will soon lead into their spectacular new music centre in Gateshead.

Andrew Manze Prom 6

The English Concert,
The Academy of Ancient Music

Hailed in the press as 'the Grappelli of the Baroque', the new Music Director of The English Concert and ex-Associate Director of The Academy of Ancient Music brings the two ensembles together with student forces for a large-scale celebration of Corelli's 350th birthday.

Marin Alsop Prom 10

Bournemouth Symphony Orchestra

Music Director Laureate of the Colorado Symphony, the New York-born Bernstein protégée has made a major impact with her recordings and concerts of American music in this country. She now makes her Proms debut with the British orchestra of which she became Principal Conductor last October.

Greg Funfgeld Prom 16

The Bach Choir of Bethlehem
The Bach Festival Orchestra

A noted organist and harpsichordist, who recently directed Bach's *Musical Offering* in collaboration with the Trisha Brown Dance Company, Greg Funfgeld has been Artistic Director of the USA's oldest Bach choir since 1983.

Christian Gansch Prom 18

BBC National Orchestra of Wales

Formerly a violinist in the Munich Philharmonic under Sergiu Celibidache and a senior record producer with Deutsche Grammophon, Austrian-born Christian Gansch has worked widely with European orchestras since making his conducting debut in Berlin in 1985.

Alan Gilbert Prom 22

Mahler Chamber Orchestra

Chief Conductor of the Royal Stockholm Philharmonic since January 2000, New Yorker Alan Gilbert originally studied violin and composition at Harvard, the Juilliard School of Music and the Curtis Institute.

Vladimir Jurowski Prom 23

Glyndebourne Festival Opera

The Moscow-born, German-trained son of a conductor, Vladimir Jurowski won much praise in his first season as Glyndebourne's new Music Director last summer and this year introduces the festival's first ever staging of a Viennese operetta.

Ilan Volkov Proms 26 & 27

BBC Scottish Symphony Orchestra

The youngest conductor ever to head up a BBC orchestra, Israeli-born Ilan Volkov gave his first concert as the new Chief Conductor of the BBC Scottish SO in February, aged only 26.

Thierry Fischer Prom 34

Ulster Orchestra

A former flautist with the Chamber Orchestra of Europe, Swiss-born Thierry Fischer has concentrated solely on conducting since 1992 and became Principal Conductor and Artistic Advisor of the Ulster Orchestra in 2001.

West-Eastern Divan Orchestra

An orchestra made up of Arab and Israeli musicians? In the current state of the Middle East, the idea seems inconceivable. Yet, as Louise Downes **reports, it has now become a reality, thanks to the vision of Daniel Barenboim**

'I have long believed that there can be no military solution to the Arab–Israeli conflict,' says pianist-conductor Daniel Barenboim, 'neither strategically nor morally. If I am right, then sooner or later the two sides will have to establish some kind of contact – cultural, economic, scientific or whatever. And really, I think, so much blood has flowed, why do we have to wait for that? Why do we have to wait for the politicians, if we can do something now?' And what Barenboim himself can do, of course, is to make music.

Hence his historic piano recital at Bir Zeit University, on the Israeli-occupied West Bank, in January 1999 – the first time an Israeli artist had ever performed on Palestinian territory. Hence too his follow-up recitals at Bir Zeit again last August and at the Palestinian National Conservatory of Music in the besieged town of Ramallah last September. 'I must say, when I came back from Ramallah, I felt good, I felt I had done something good. I had played for Palestinian children, for many of whom it was the first time they ever had a positive thought about anything to do with Israel. As one girl told me – she must have been 14 or 15 years old – "I'm glad you came, because until now I only ever saw Israeli tanks and Israeli soldiers, and now I see an Israeli musician." I really felt I had achieved something positive.'

It's the same positive feeling, but on an even larger scale, that inspired the creation of the West-Eastern Divan. A remarkable orchestra made up of young Arab and Israeli musicians, it first came together – under the joint aegis of the Israeli conductor and his close friend, the Palestinian cultural philosopher Edward W. Said – for three weeks of shared music-making and cross-cultural discussions in Weimar in 1999 and has since become an annual event.

Named after the great German poet (and Weimar resident) Johann Wolfgang von Goethe's pioneering late collection of Persian-inspired verses – then, and now, unique in its fusion of Islamic and Western styles and sensibilities – the West-Eastern Divan Orchestra offers an inspiring but unsentimental musical paradigm of a future peace, with roughly equal numbers of young Israeli and Arab musicians from all across the Middle East (and all ages from 13 to 26) coming together on neutral soil, if not in the rose-tinted 'perfect harmony' hymned by TV cola ads, at least to share food, views, living-space and, perhaps most importantly of all, music stands.

For, as Barenboim observes – citing just one example of two cellists, one Syrian, one Israeli, who had never before met anyone from 'the other side' until they found themselves seated at the same music stand – 'Once you've done that, once you've tried to play the same note, with the same dynamic, the same attack, the same vibrato – well, once you've done that, you can never look at one another in the same way again, because you can only do that by adjusting to your neighbour, by sharing a common experience.'

'It doesn't pretend to be building bridges and all that hokey stuff,' says Said. 'But there it is: a paradigm of coherent and intelligent living together.'

And, as if to prove that their dream of peaceful co-existence really can become a reality, this year's sessions will be held, as they were last year, at a former Catholic seminary near Seville, in the very heart of the fabled Moorish kingdom of Al-Andaluz – 'the only place in the world,' Barenboim points out, 'where Jewish and Arab people ever lived together in peace for 700 years'.

West-Eastern Divan Orchestra
Prom 44 Friday 22 August, 7.30pm

ABOVE
Daniel Barenboim rehearses the young players of the West-Eastern Divan

ABOVE
Johann Wolfgang von Goethe (1749–1832), the German poet whose pioneering collection of Persian-inspired verses lent Barenboim's Arab-Israeli youth orchestra its name

How to book

Your copy of the *BBC Proms 2003 Guide* contains a tear-out form for Priority Booking. For your best chance of securing the tickets you want, fill it in and post or fax it to arrive at the Royal Albert Hall Box Office by Monday 19 May.

You can also use the Online Ticket Request system for Priority Booking. Visit the BBC Proms website for details: www.bbc.co.uk/proms

The Box Office will begin issuing tickets on Monday 19 May; all bookings received before this date will be treated as if they had arrived on that day. All Priority Bookings, whether sent by post, fax or Online, are processed simultaneously and no method receives preference. Note that the Online Ticket Request option is not a 'real time' booking system.

Express Bookings will be handled first – for full details see page 121.

Note that until General Booking opens on Monday 16 June, only bookings made on the official Priority Booking Form or via the Online Ticket Request system will be accepted.

The Last Night of the Proms
Because of the high demand for tickets, special booking arrangements apply. See page 119

Special Offers
For Special Offers, see pages 112–113.

Priority Booking
By post, fax and online – opens Monday 19 May
Use the Priority Booking Form or visit www.bbc.co.uk/proms

To take advantage of the Priority Booking period – and enjoy your best chance of securing the seats you want – use the official Priority Booking Form (facing page 122) or visit the Proms website. Note that all postal, fax and online bookings received before Monday 19 May will be treated as if they had arrived on that date.

Postal address: BBC Proms, Box Office, Royal Albert Hall, London SW7 2AP
Fax number: 020 7581 9311   Online booking: www.bbc.co.uk/proms

General Booking
In person, by phone or online – opens Monday 16 June
The Box Office is located at Door 12 of the Royal Albert Hall and is open 9.00am–9.00pm daily. Note that no booking fee applies to tickets bought in person at the Hall.

Telephone number: 020 7589 8212   Online booking: www.bbc.co.uk/proms

Last Night Ballot
Exclusive to readers of the *BBC Proms 2003 Guide*

Your chance to enter this year's Last Night Ballot and apply for tickets to the Last Night. See page 119.

Promming on the Day
Don't book, just turn up

Up to 1,400 standing places are available at each Proms concert. Season Tickets and Weekend Promming Passes can be booked in advance: see page 118. Additionally, over 500 Arena and Gallery tickets are always on sale at the door from an hour beforehand, so you can just turn up on the night.

BOOKING

Special Offers

For full details of all Special Offers, see pages 112–13

Proms Odyssey

Choose three or more concerts from our special Greek myth-based selection and save up to 30%, and receive free programme vouchers as well.

Weekend Promming Pass

Beat the queues and save money too.

Same Day Savers

Book for two concerts on the same day and save £4.00.

Group Bookings

Book 10 or more Centre/Side Stalls or Front/Rear Circle tickets for any Prom in the A, B, D or E price bands and save 10%; save 5% on C-band concerts.

Under-16s

Save 50% on seats for marked concerts.

Proms Extras: venue codes

BM • British Museum
RAH • Royal Albert Hall (Auditorium)
RCA • Royal College of Art
RCM • Royal College of Music
V&A • Victoria & Albert Museum

All concert details were correct at the time of going to press. The BBC reserves the right to alter artist or programme details as necessary

---

PROM 1

Friday 18 July
7.30pm – c9.45pm
Price Code **B**

Shostakovich
Festive Overture   7'

Tchaikovsky
Piano Concerto No. 1
in B flat minor   36'

interval

Prokofiev, arr. Stassevich
Ivan the Terrible – oratorio   60'

Lang Lang *piano*
Irina Tchistyakova *mezzo-soprano*
James Rutherford *baritone*

BBC Symphony Chorus
BBC National Chorus of Wales
BBC Symphony Orchestra
Leonard Slatkin *conductor*

The BBC Symphony Orchestra and two BBC choruses under Chief Conductor Leonard Slatkin launch the 2003 Proms with anniversary composer Prokofiev's dramatic score for Sergey Eisenstein's *Ivan the Terrible* (see *Prokofiev*, pages 36–8). After his sensational Proms debut two years ago, the amazing young Chinese pianist Lang Lang returns to tackle another pinnacle of the Romantic repertoire.

This concert will be broadcast on BBC2

🔊 **6.00pm Pre-Prom Talk** (RCM) Dennis Marks on *Ivan the Terrible*

NOTE TIME PROM 2

Saturday 19 July
7.00pm – c9.30pm
Price Code **A**

The Nation's Favourite Prom

Berlioz
The Damnation of Faust –
Hungarian March   5'
Arias & duets chosen by you   c15'

Prokofiev
Peter and the Wolf*   25'

interval

Walton
Façade – excerpts   10'

Vaughan Williams
The Lark Ascending   14'

Britten
Folk Song arrangements   10'

Khachaturian
Spartacus – Suite No. 2   21'

Rosemary Joshua *soprano*
John Mark Ainsley *tenor*
Janine Jansen *violin*
Sir David Attenborough *narrator**

BBC Concert Orchestra
Barry Wordsworth *conductor*

Popular classics, and a chance for you, the audience, to choose the items for two top British opera stars to sing – see page 129 for how to vote.

This concert will be broadcast on BBC1

🔊 **10.00am Greek Myths Study Day** (BM) See page 134

NOTE TIME PROM 3

Sunday 20 July
7.00pm – c10.00pm
Price Code **A**

Tippett
King Priam   128'

David Wilson-Johnson *Priam*
Elizabeth Connell *Hecuba/Athene*
Susan Bickley *Andromache/Hera*
Susan Parry *Helen/Aphrodite*
Marcel Reijans *Paris*
Martyn Hill *Achilles*
Stephen Roberts *Patroclus*
William Dazeley *Hector*
Timothy Robinson *Hermes*
Christine Rice *Nurse*
Christopher Gillett *Young Guard*
Stephen Richardson *Old Man*
James Eager *Paris as a boy*

BBC Singers
BBC National Orchestra of Wales
David Atherton *conductor*

David Wilson-Johnson

We launch this season's exploration of Greek myths (see pages 4–23) with a concert performance of Tippett's epic opera, based on Homer's account of the Trojan War and here conducted by David Atherton, a long-time champion of the work.

There will be two intervals

🔊 **5.30pm Pre-Prom Talk** (RAH) Meirion Bowen on *King Priam*

Every Prom live on BBC Radio 3 and www.bbc.co.uk/proms

PROM 4

NOTE TIME

Monday 21 July
7.00pm – c9.15pm
Price Code **A**

Beethoven
The Creatures of Prometheus –
Overture   6'

Brahms
Piano Concerto No. 1 in D minor   44'

interval

Rakhmaninov
Symphony No. 2 in E minor   55'

Stephen Hough piano

Budapest Festival Orchestra
Iván Fischer conductor

Iván Fischer

The next Greek myth in this year's survey (see pages 4–23) is that of Prometheus, the Titan who stole fire from Heaven and gave it to Man. The first of this year's visiting orchestras makes a welcome return, along with its founder-conductor, to perform Rakhmaninov's gloriously romantic Second Symphony. British pianist Stephen Hough joins them as the soloist in Brahms's monumental First Piano Concerto.

This concert will be broadcast on BBC4

♪ **1.00pm Proms Chamber Music**
See pages 110–11

PROM 5

LATE NIGHT

Monday 21 July
10.00pm – c11.30pm
Price Code **D**

Bach
Concerto in C minor for oboe
and violin, after BWV 1060   15'

Philip Cashian
Tableaux   c15'
world premiere

Veress
Passacaglia concertante for oboe
and orchestra   18'

Stravinsky
Apollon musagète   30'

Heinz Holliger oboe

Northern Sinfonia
Thomas Zehetmair director/violin

The Northern Sinfonia returns with its new Music Director, well known to Proms audiences as a violinist. Together, they present the first of this year's world premieres (see New Music, pages 66–75) and Stravinsky's neo-classical ballet about the Greek god Apollo (see Season Theme, pages 4–23). The Swiss oboist Heinz Holliger is the soloist in a concertante work written specially for him and also joins Zehetmair for a double concerto by Bach.

There will be no interval

PROM 6

16

Tuesday 22 July
7.30pm – c9.30pm
Price Code **A**

Corelli
Concerto grosso in D major,
Op. 6 No. 4   9'

Handel
Motet 'Silete venti'   25'

Corelli
Concerto grosso in G minor,
Op. 6 No. 8, 'Christmas Concerto' 13'

interval

Handel
Dixit Dominus   33'

Sarah Fox soprano
Julia Gooding soprano
Sarah Connolly mezzo-soprano
Mark Le Brocq tenor
Matthew Hargreaves bass

Choir of The English Concert
Chorus of The Academy
of Ancient Music
The English Concert
The Academy of Ancient Music
Musicians from the
Royal Academy of Music
Andrew Manze director/violin

Two leading Baroque orchestras and a new crop of period instrumentalists celebrate the 350th anniversary of Corelli with music on a grand scale.

This concert will be broadcast on BBC4

💬 **6.00pm Pre-Prom Talk** (RAH)
Nicholas Kenyon and Andrew Manze

PROM 7

NOTE TIME

Wednesday 23 July
7.00pm – c9.05pm
Price Code **A**

Haydn
Symphony No. 104 in D major,
'London'   30'

Schuman
A Song of Orpheus   17'

interval

Vaughan Williams
A London Symphony   45'

Paul Watkins cello

BBC Symphony Orchestra
Leonard Slatkin conductor

Two 'London' symphonies – from the late 18th and early 20th centuries – evoke very different pictures of the capital's vitality and variety. They
Paul Watkins
frame a modern American composer's Shakespeare-inspired rhapsody on one of the most famous, and musically influential, of all Greek myths (see pages 4–23). Soloist Paul Watkins was formerly Principal Cellist with the BBC Symphony Orchestra.

This concert will be broadcast on BBC4

PROM 8
LATE NIGHT

Wednesday 23 July
10.00pm – c11.25pm
Price Code **E**

Mendelssohn
Antigone – incidental music
to the tragedy of Sophocles
(*performed in English*)   *c80'*

Zoë Waites *Antigone*
Brian Protheroe *Creon*

Stephan Loges *baritone*
Roderick Williams *baritone*

Eugenia Arsenis *director*
BBC Singers (men's voices)
City of London Sinfonia
Richard Hickox *conductor*

Mendelssohn is justly famous for his
music to Shakespeare's *A Midsummer
Night's Dream*, but he also wrote
several scores to accompany the great
Greek tragedies (*see Season Theme,
pages 4–23*). The concluding part
of Sophocles' 'Theban Trilogy', and
therefore a sequel to *Oedipus rex*
(*see Prom 65*), *Antigone* dramatises
the tragic results that ensue when
one woman's conscience clashes with
the letter of the law. In this specially
devised performance, Mendelssohn's
overture and choruses are set in a
theatrical context based on Sophocles'
original text.

*Zoë Waites and Brian Protheroe appear
subject to availability*

PROM 9

Thursday 24 July
7.30pm – c9.35pm
Price Code **A**

James MacMillan
Symphony No. 3, 'Silence'*   *c35'*
*BBC/NHK co-commission:
European premiere*

R. Strauss
Four Last Songs   *24'*

interval

Beethoven
Symphony No. 5 in C minor   *33'*

Barbara Frittoli *soprano*

BBC Philharmonic
James MacMillan *conductor**
Gianandrea Noseda *conductor*

Gianandrea Noseda conducts
Beethoven's compelling symphonic
journey from darkness to triumph,
prefaced by the European premiere
of the latest symphony by the BBC
Philharmonic's Composer/Conductor
(*see New Music, pages 66–75*).
Acclaimed Italian soprano Barbara
Frittoli makes her Proms debut in
Strauss's elegiac *Four Last Songs*.

This concert will be broadcast on BBC4

🗨 **6.00pm Pre-Prom Talk** (RAH)
James MacMillan on his Symphony No. 3

PROM 10

Friday 25 July
7.30pm – c9.30pm
Price Code **A**

Tchaikovsky
Francesca da Rimini   *22'*

Joe Duddell
Ruby   *c25'*
BBC commission: world premiere

interval

Bartók
Concerto for Orchestra   *36'*

Colin Currie *percussion*

Bournemouth Symphony Orchestra
Marin Alsop *conductor*

The Bournemouth Symphony
Orchestra's new Principal Conductor,
Marin Alsop, makes her Proms debut
in Tchaikovsky's brooding tone poem
and Bartók's orchestral showpiece.
The brilliant young percussionist Colin
Currie, the first ever percussion finalist
in the BBC Young Musician of the Year
competition, is the soloist in a brand-
new concerto by Joe Duddell (*see New
Music, pages 66–75*).

This concert will be broadcast on BBC4

🗨 **6.00pm Pre-Prom Talk** (RAH)
Joe Duddell and Colin Currie
talk to Verity Sharp

🗨 **c9.45pm Proms Question
Time** (RAH) *See page 129*

PROM 11
NOTE TIME

Saturday 26 July
11.00am – c12.45pm
Price Code **G**

**Blue Peter Prom –
Magical Journeys**
A colourful programme
for all the family

Konnie Huq *presenter*
Simon Thomas *presenter*
Julian Bliss *clarinet*
STOMP

New London Children's Choir
BBC Philharmonic
Jason Lai *conductor*
Gianandrea Noseda *conductor*

This year's *Blue Peter* concert takes up
the *Odyssey* theme of this year's Proms
and creates a magical journey through
a wonderful universe of music that
includes John Williams's *Harry Potter:
The Chamber of Secrets*, Holst's *Mars*
from *The Planets*, the brilliant talent
of young clarinettist Julian Bliss in his
Proms debut, the sound and energy
of the acclaimed music and dance
phenomenon STOMP and the
traditional Proms climax of Elgar's
Pomp and Circumstance March No. 1.
Blue Peter's Konnie and Simon will be
our guides through this colourful
collection of pieces, and will make
sure we sing and stomp in time along
with the BBC Philharmonic.

There will be one interval

PROM 12

Saturday 26 July
7.30pm – c9.35pm
Price Code **A**

Colin Matthews
Vivo   5'
London premiere

Berlioz
Les nuits d'été   30'

interval

Elgar
Symphony No. 1 in A flat major   52'

Alice Coote *mezzo-soprano*

Hallé Orchestra
Mark Elder *conductor*

Mark Elder

The Hallé's relationship with its Music Director Mark Elder is going from strength to strength. Together, they perform one of the greatest of all British symphonies, a work premiered by this orchestra in Manchester 95 years ago. It is prefaced by the London premiere of Hallé Associate Composer Colin Matthews's virtuosic curtain-raiser (see *New Music, pages 66–75*) and bicentenary composer Berlioz's ravishing song-cycle (see *Berlioz, pages 30–32*), featuring Radio 3 New Generation Artist Alice Coote, who also gives a Proms Chamber Music recital in August (see *PCM 4*).

This concert will be broadcast on BBC4

PROM 13

Sunday 27 July
7.30pm – c9.30pm
Price Code **A**

Haydn
Symphony No. 44 in E minor,
'Trauer'   22'

Bartók
Piano Concerto No. 3   23'

interval

Copland
Quiet City   10'

John Adams
On the Transmigration of Souls   24'
European premiere

Hélène Grimaud *piano*

Southend Girls' Choir
Southend Boys' Choir
BBC Symphony Chorus
BBC Symphony Orchestra
John Adams *conductor*

John Adams was recently appointed as the BBC Symphony Orchestra's Artist-in-Association and brings to the Proms the work he composed in response to the 9/11 tragedy (see *New Music, pages 66–75*) coupled with music by Copland, Bartók and Haydn.

This concert will be broadcast on BBC4

♪ **4.00–10.30pm Memory Spaces (RCA)** See page 132

💬 **6.00pm Pre-Prom Talk (RCM)**
John Adams in conversation

PROM 14

Monday 28 July
7.30pm – c9.15pm
Price Code **B**

Berlioz
The Childhood of Christ
(sung in French)   95'

Bernarda Fink *Mary*
James Gilchrist *Narrator*
Gilles Cachemaille *Joseph*
Jeremy White *Herod/Father of the Family*

Monteverdi Choir
Choir of Clare College, Cambridge
Orchestre Révolutionnaire et Romantique
Sir John Eliot Gardiner *conductor*

Our bicentenary celebration of Berlioz (see *pages 30–32*) continues with his 'sacred trilogy' *The Childhood of Christ*, which started out as a playful exercise in antique style and grew into one of the composer's most popular and heartfelt scores. It is conducted by a pioneer in the period-instrument performance of Romantic repertoire.

There will be no interval

This concert will be broadcast on BBC4

♪ **1.00pm Proms Chamber Music**
See pages 110–11

💬 **6.00pm Pre-Prom Talk (RCM)**
Sir John Eliot Gardiner on Berlioz

PROM 15

Tuesday 29 July
7.00pm – c8.55pm
Price Code **B**

R. Strauss
Elektra *(sung in German)*   105'

Gabriele Schnaut *Electra*
Janice Watson *Chrysothemis*
Felicity Palmer *Clytemnestra*
John Treleaven *Aegisthus*
Alan Held *Orestes*
Susan Gorton *First Maid*
Antonia Sotgiu *Second Maid*
Sarah Castle *Third Maid*
Gweneth-Ann Jeffers *Fourth Maid*
Rebecca Nash *Fifth Maid*
Mary Lloyd Davies *Overseer*
Huw Rhys-Evans *Young Servant*

London Voices
BBC Scottish Symphony Orchestra
Donald Runnicles *conductor*

We continue our exploration of the great Greek myths (see *pages 4–23*) with Strauss's harrowing and bloody operatic thriller, conducted by the Scottish-born Music Director of the San Francisco Opera. Gabriele Schnaut, who recently performed the role at New York's Metropolitan Opera, sings the part of the vengeful princess whose one purpose in life is to murder her mother.

There will be no interval

This concert will be broadcast on BBC4

💬 **5.30pm Pre-Prom Talk (RCM)**
Rodney Milnes on *Elektra*

PROM 16
LATE NIGHT

Tuesday 29 July
10.00pm – c11.30pm
Price Code **D**

Bach
Cantata No. 191, 'Gloria in
excelsis Deo'   20'

Mendelssohn
Motet 'Jauchzet dem Herrn
alle Welt'   5'

Psalm 43 'Richte mich, Gott'   4'

Motet 'Herr, nun lassest du deinem
Diener in Frieden fahren'   5'

Zum Abendsegen 'Herr, sei gnädig
unserm Flehn'   2'

Libby Larsen
I It Am   c15'
*BBC/Bach Choir co-commission:
world premiere*

Bach
Cantata No. 34, 'O ewiges Feuer' 21'

Tamara Matthews soprano
Rosa Lamoreaux soprano
Daniel Taylor counter-tenor
Benjamin Butterfield tenor
Daniel Lichti bass-baritone

The Bach Choir of Bethlehem
The Bach Festival Orchestra
Greg Funfgeld conductor

Two of Bach's most thrilling cantatas
frame choral music by the composer
who headed the 19th-century Bach
revival. The Pennsylvania-based Bach
Choir celebrates its first UK tour with
a specially commissioned work (see
New Music, pages 66–75).

PROM 17

Wednesday 30 July
7.30pm – c9.55pm
Price Code **A**

In the presence of
Her Majesty The Queen
and HRH The Duke
of Edinburgh

The National Anthem	3'

Walton
Coronation Te Deum   8'

Elgar
Sea Pictures   23'

Grainger
Molly on the Shore   4'

Shepherd's Hey   3'

interval

Mark-Anthony Turnage
Momentum   10'

Tippett
Dance, Clarion Air   5'

Bax
November Woods   15'

Britten
The Young Person's Guide to
the Orchestra   18'

Catherine Wyn-Rogers mezzo-soprano

Choristers of Winchester Cathedral
Winchester College Quiristers
**Members of Eton College
Chapel Choir**
BBC Singers
BBC Symphony Chorus
BBC Symphony Orchestra
Sir Andrew Davis conductor

Following the success of 'Prom at the Palace', last summer's Royal Jubilee concert
conducted by Sir Andrew Davis in the grounds of Buckingham Palace, HM The
Queen and HRH The Duke of Edinburgh visit the Royal Albert Hall to attend a
special Prom celebrating this year's 50th anniversary of Her Majesty's Coronation.
Combined BBC forces join the choristers of three of England's leading institutions
in a wide-ranging collection of British and Commonwealth music, including works
by Tippett and Walton specially written for Coronation year.

This concert will be broadcast on BBC4

PROM 18
NOTE TIME

Thursday 31 July
7.00pm – c8.55pm
Price Code **A**

György Ligeti
Lontano   11'

Mozart
Violin Concerto No. 5 in A major,
K219 'Turkish'   30'

interval

Beethoven
Symphony No. 6 in F major,
'Pastoral'   39'

Antje Weithaas violin

BBC National Orchestra of Wales
Christian Gansch conductor

Christian Gansch makes his Proms
debut with the BBC National
Orchestra of Wales, with which he has
been building up a strong relationship.
Ligeti's *Lontano* is the first in a sequence
of works celebrating the composer's
80th birthday (see *Ligeti, pages 42–3*).
Antje Weithaas returns to the Proms
in Mozart's sunny concerto, and
the concert closes with Beethoven's
evergreen and deeply spiritual outing
to the countryside.

This concert will be broadcast on BBC4

PROM 19

Friday 1 August
7.30pm – c9.35pm
Price Code **A**

Musorgsky, orch. Rimsky-Korsakov
Night on a Bare Mountain   *12'*

Erkki-Sven Tüür
Violin Concerto   *33'*
London premiere

interval

Prokofiev
Symphony No. 6 in E flat minor   *43'*

Isabelle van Keulen *violin*

BBC Philharmonic
Paavo Järvi *conductor*

Isabelle van Keulen

The Estonian conductor Paavo Järvi returns to the Proms with the BBC Philharmonic to conduct the London premiere of the Violin Concerto by his compatriot Erkki-Sven Tüür, with the violinist Isabelle van Keulen, who gave the work's world premiere in Frankfurt in 1999 (see *New Music, pages 66–75*). Framing it are two Russian works: Musorgsky's heady witches' brew and anniversary composer Prokofiev's rarely-performed, and darkly tragic, Sixth Symphony.

This concert will be broadcast on BBC4

🎤 **6.00pm Pre-Prom Talk (RAH)**
Erkki-Sven Tüür and Andrew Kurowski

PROM 20

NOTE TIME

Saturday 2 August
6.30pm – c8.45pm
Price Code **A**

HK Gruber
Dancing in the Dark*   *22'*
UK premiere

Prokofiev
Piano Concerto No. 3 in C major   *27'*

interval

Tchaikovsky
Symphony No. 5 in E minor   *50'*

Nelson Goerner *piano*

BBC Philharmonic
HK Gruber *conductor**
Vassily Sinaisky *conductor*

The unique Viennese composer, conductor and *chansonnier* HK Gruber directs the UK premiere of his own new work (see *New Music, pages 66–75*). Rising young virtuoso Nelson Goerner makes his Proms debut in anniversary composer Prokofiev's best-known piano concerto. The BBC Philharmonic's Russian-born Principal Guest Conductor, Vassily Sinaisky, conducts Tchaikovsky's impassioned and intense Fifth Symphony.

Nelson Goerner

This concert will be broadcast on BBC4

PROM 21

LATE NIGHT

Saturday 2 August
10.00pm – c2.00am
Price Code **E**

The Late 'Late Junction' Prom

Jazz Jamaica All Stars
Koçani Orkestar
Kimmo Pohjonen *accordion*
Arto Tuncboyacian *percussion*
Manecas Costa *guitar*
Ellika and Solo *voice/fiddle/kora*

Inspired by the eclectic mix of BBC Radio 3's *Late Junction*, and framed by the pulsating rhythms of the Jazz Jamaica All Stars, this specially extended Late Night Prom will be a free-flowing event, combining solo and duet work with big set-pieces, all linked by DJs Rita Ray and Max Reinhardt from The Shrine (see *Season Highlights, page 57*). Come and go as you will during four hours of brilliantly diverse music-making from around the world.

PROM 22

Sunday 3 August
7.30pm – c9.40pm
Price Code **B**

Ravel
Le tombeau de Couperin   *17'*

Mozart
Piano Concerto No. 9 in E flat major, K271 'Jeunehomme'   *32'*

interval

Mendelssohn
Symphony No. 3 in A minor, 'Scottish'   *40'*

Leif Ove Andsnes *piano*

Mahler Chamber Orchestra
Alan Gilbert *conductor*

Leif Ove Andsnes

The Mahler Chamber Orchestra, founded in 1997 by Claudio Abbado, and American conductor Alan Gilbert both make Proms debuts this season. They perform Ravel's tribute to a great Baroque master and Mendelssohn's symphonic postcard from Scotland, and are joined by the star of last year's Last Night for Mozart's early concerto masterpiece.

This concert will be broadcast on BBC4

🎤 **5.30pm Proms Lecture (V&A)**
Peter Sellars: 'The Culture of Democracy'. *See page 133*

PROM 23

NOTE TIME

Monday 4 August
7.00pm – c10.00pm
Price Code **C**

J. Strauss II
Die Fledermaus
(sung in German; semi-staged)   150'

Pamela Armstrong Rosalinde
Lyubov Petrova Adele
Malena Ernman Prince Orlofsky
Pär Lindskog Alfred
Sir Thomas Allen Eisenstein
Håkan Hagegård Dr Falke
Artur Korn Frank
Udo Samuel Frosch
Ragnar Ulfung Dr Blind

Stephen Lawless director
Glyndebourne Festival Chorus
London Philharmonic Orchestra
Vladimir Jurowski conductor

Pamela Armstrong

For its annual visit to the Proms, Glyndebourne Festival Opera – under its new Russian-born Music Director, Vladimir Jurowski – brings its first ever production of Johann Strauss's flighty comedy of revenge, disguise and infidelity (see Season Highlights, page 53).

There will be one interval

♪ **1.00pm Proms Chamber Music**
See pages 110–11

🔊 **5.30pm Pre-Prom Talk (RAH)**
Patrick O'Connor on Die Fledermaus

PROM 24

Tuesday 5 August
7.30pm – c9.50pm
Price Code **A**

R. Strauss
Die Liebe der Danae – Symphonic
Fragment   9'

An den Baum Daphne*   23'

interval

R. Strauss
Der Rosenkavalier – excerpts   70'

Dame Anne Evans Marschallin
Susan Gritton Sophie
Katarina Karnéus Octavian

**Choristers of King's College,
Cambridge**
BBC Singers
BBC Symphony Orchestra
Stephen Cleobury conductor*
Sir Charles Mackerras conductor

Richard Strauss was one of the 20th-century composers most engaged with Greek myths and their retelling (see Season Theme, pages 4–23). Sir Charles Mackerras conducts a sensuous fragment drawn from the composer's penultimate, posthumously premiered opera on the legend of Danae, plus his own selection of highlights from Strauss's most popular opera. In between, Stephen Cleobury conducts the two choirs of which he is Music Director in the unaccompanied chorus that Strauss wrote as a pendant to his mythological opera Daphne.

PROM 25

 [16]

Wednesday 6 August
7.30pm – c9.30pm
Price Code **A**

Coles
Overture 'A Comedy of Errors'   11'

Sally Beamish
Trumpet Concerto   c20'
London premiere

interval

Elgar
Symphony No. 2 in E flat major   55'

Håkan Hardenberger trumpet

**National Youth Orchestra
of Scotland**
Martyn Brabbins conductor

Håkan Hardenberger

Born in Scotland in 1888, Cecil Coles was among the talented composers who died in the First World War. Martyn Brabbins, who has been recording his works, brings his Shakespearian overture to the Proms, along with Elgar's great Second Symphony. Sally Beamish's new concerto was composed especially for Håkan Hardenberger and the National Youth Orchestra of Scotland (see New Music, pages 66–75).

🔊 **6.00pm Pre-Prom Talk (RAH)**
Sally Beamish and Håkan Hardenberger talk to Stephen Johnson

PROM 26

Thursday 7 August
7.30pm – c9.30pm
Price Code **A**

Judith Weir
The Welcome Arrival of Rain   16'
UK premiere

Schumann
Cello Concerto in A minor   25'

interval

Shostakovich
Symphony No. 10 in E minor   45'

Heinrich Schiff cello

BBC Scottish Symphony Orchestra
Ilan Volkov conductor

Heinrich Schiff

In the first of two concerts with its new Chief Conductor, the BBC Scottish Symphony Orchestra pairs Shostakovich's acerbic Tenth Symphony, first performed shortly after the death of Stalin 50 years ago, with a new work by Judith Weir, inspired by an ancient Hindu text (see New Music, pages 66–75) and premiered in Minnesota by Osmo Vänskä, Ilan Volkov's predecessor as the BBC SSO's Chief Conductor. Heinrich Schiff is the soloist in Schumann's Cello Concerto.

♪ **6.00pm Composer Portrait**
Judith Weir. See page 136

Ken Howard Klaus Rudolph

PROM 27

Friday 8 August
7.00pm – c9.05pm
Price Code **A**

György Ligeti
San Francisco Polyphony   *12'*

Beethoven
Piano Concerto No. 1 in C major   *36'*

interval

Brahms
Symphony No. 4 in E minor   *40'*

Stephen Kovacevich *piano*

BBC Scottish Symphony Orchestra
Ilan Volkov *conductor*

Stephen Kovacevich

Brahms's final symphony, with its famous last-movement chaconne, sits alongside the densely-woven counterpoint of featured composer György Ligeti's *San Francisco Polyphony*. Stephen Kovacevich makes a welcome return to the Proms as soloist in Beethoven's early piano concerto.

💬 **5.30pm Pre-Prom Talk** (RCM)
Richard Steinitz on Ligeti

PROM 28

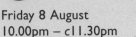

Friday 8 August
10.00pm – c11.30pm
Price Code **D**

Stravinsky
Ebony Concerto   *9'*

Peter Eötvös
Snatches of a Conversation   *11'*
UK premiere

Detlev Glanert
Secret Room   *8'*

Elliott Carter
Clarinet Concerto   *18'*

György Ligeti
Aventures; Nouvelles aventures   *23'*

Michael Collins *clarinet*
Marco Blaauw *trumpet*
Barbara Hannigan *soprano*
Mary King *mezzo-soprano*
Omar Ebrahim *baritone/speaker*

London Sinfonietta
Peter Eötvös *conductor*

Peter Eötvös introduces his whimsical new work for trumpet and speaker (see *New Music*, pages 66–75), alongside Detlev Glanert's highly praised *Secret Room* and clarinet concertos by Stravinsky and Elliott Carter (who turns 95 in December). Our celebration of Ligeti's 80th birthday (see *Ligeti*, pages 42–3) continues with his wild and wonderful adventures in sound.

There will be no interval

PROM 29

Saturday 9 August
7.00pm – c9.15pm
Price Code **A**

Messiaen
Les offrandes oubliées   *10'*

Berlioz
Harold in Italy   *42'*

interval

Prokofiev
Symphony No. 5 in B flat major   *46'*

Lawrence Power *viola*

National Youth Orchestra
of Great Britain
Yan Pascal Tortelier *conductor*

The National Youth Orchestra of Great Britain pays its annual visit to the Proms under a familiar French conductor. Messiaen's early 'symphonic meditation' prefaces works by our two major anniversary composers: Prokofiev's rousingly popular Fifth Symphony and Berlioz's Byronic concerto, *Harold in Italy* (see *Berlioz*, pages 30–32), featuring Radio 3 New Generation Artist Lawrence Power.

This concert will be broadcast on BBC2

PROM 30

Sunday 10 August
7.30pm – c9.45pm
Price Code **A**

Poulenc
La voix humaine (*sung in French*)   *46'*

interval

Stravinsky
Perséphone (*performed in French*)   *54'*

Dame Felicity Lott *soprano*
Paul Groves *tenor*

Trinity Boys' Choir
Cantate Youth Choir
BBC Symphony Chorus
BBC Symphony Orchestra
Sir Andrew Davis *conductor*

Dame Felicity Lott

Sir Andrew Davis conducts two masterpieces of 20th-century French music-theatre, both featuring females *in extremis*. Poulenc's one-woman *tour de force*, to a text by Jean Cocteau, is sung by Dame Felicity Lott (see *Season Highlights*, page 54). Stravinsky's multi-media melodrama, to a text by André Gide, reworks an ancient Greek fertility myth in Christian terms (see *Season Theme*, pages 4–23).

💬 **6.00pm Pre-Prom Talk** (RAH)
Stephen Walsh on *Perséphone* and *La voix humaine*

PROM 31

NOTE TIME

Monday 11 August
7.00pm – c9.00pm
Price Code A

R. Strauss
Tod und Verklärung   23'

Mahler
Rückert-Lieder   22'

interval

Prokofiev
Alexander Nevsky – cantata   40'

Ekaterina Gubanova *mezzo-soprano*
Detlef Roth *baritone*

London Philharmonic Choir
Crouch End Festival Chorus
Royal Philharmonic Orchestra
Daniele Gatti *conductor*

Daniele Gatti

The Royal Philharmonic and its Music Director Daniele Gatti mark the Prokofiev anniversary with music from his film score for Eisenstein's powerful epic about a medieval Russian hero's defeat of German invaders. Strauss's richly-scored tone poem prefaces Mahler's deeply-felt song-cycle.

♪ **1.00pm Proms Chamber Music**
See pages 110–11

💬 **5.30pm Pre-Prom Talk (RCM)**
Marina Frolova-Walker on Prokofiev's *Alexander Nevsky*

PROM 32

LATE NIGHT

Monday 11 August
10.00pm – c11.25pm
Price Code D

Krzysztof Penderecki
Sinfonietta for strings   12'

Mark O'Connor
Violin Concerto No. 6, 'Old Brass' c25'
world premiere

Bartók
Divertimento   25'

Mark O'Connor *violin*

Academy of St Martin in the Fields
Kenneth Sillito *director*

The star funk-folk fiddler Mark O'Connor has been increasingly involved in mixing country and classical styles. In this concert he and the Academy of St Martin in the Fields introduce his new concerto (see *New Music, pages 66–75*), alongside Penderecki's Sinfonietta (in honour of the Polish composer's 70th birthday) and Bartók's string orchestra classic.

There will be no interval

PROM 33

Tuesday 12 August
7.30pm – c9.45pm
Price Code B

Rameau
Hippolyte et Aricie – suite   30'

Sibelius
Violin Concerto in D minor   31'

interval

Beethoven
Symphony No. 7 in A major   36'

Viktoria Mullova *violin*

Deutsche Kammerphilharmonie Bremen
Daniel Harding *conductor*

Viktoria Mullova

A leading German chamber orchestra visits the Proms with its young British music director. A terpsichorean suite by Rameau – from an opera based on the myth of Phaedra (see *Season Theme, pages 4–23*) – and Beethoven's 'apotheosis of the dance' frame a Finnish concerto whose final movement was once famously described as 'a polonaise for polar bears'. The acclaimed violinist Viktoria Mullova is the soloist.

This concert will be broadcast on BBC1

PROM 34

Wednesday 13 August
7.30pm – c9.40pm
Price Code A

Mozart
Idomeneo – Overture and ballet music (excerpts)   15'

Prokofiev
Cello Concerto   38'

interval

Kevin Volans
Strip-Weave   9'
world premiere of revised version

Sibelius
Symphony No. 5 in E flat major   30'

Li-Wei *cello*

Ulster Orchestra
Thierry Fischer *conductor*

Thierry Fischer makes his Proms debut, with the Northern Ireland orchestra of which he is Principal Conductor, in music from Mozart's mythological opera about the Cretan king Idomeneo (see *Season Theme, pages 4–23*), a new work by Irish-based composer Kevin Volans (see *New Music, pages 66–75*), and Sibelius's expansive Fifth Symphony. Radio 3 New Generation Artist Li-Wei also makes his Proms debut in the rarely-performed Cello Concerto by anniversary composer Prokofiev (see *Prokofiev, pages 36–8*).

Every Prom live on BBC Radio 3 and www.bbc.co.uk/proms

PROM 35

NOTE TIME

Thursday 14 August
7.00pm – c8.50pm
Price Code **A**

Chopin, arr. Stravinsky
Nocturne in A flat major,
Op. 32 No. 2   7'
UK premiere

Waltz in E flat major, Op. 18,
'Grande valse brillante'   7'

Oliver Knussen
Violin Concerto   18'
London premiere

interval

Elliott Carter
Boston Concerto   c15'
European premiere

Stravinsky
Agon   23'

Pinchas Zukerman *violin*

BBC Symphony Orchestra
Oliver Knussen *conductor*

Oliver Knussen directs the London
premiere of his own Violin Concerto,
with the star soloist who gave its world
premiere, and the European premiere of
Elliott Carter's new *Boston Concerto* (see
New Music, pages 66–75). These works
are framed by Stravinsky's first and last
dance scores: a little-known pair of
Chopin arrangements from 1909 and his
great Greek-inspired ballet from 1957.

💬 **5.30pm Pre-Prom Talk** (RCM)
Gillian Moore on Knussen and Carter

PROM 36

LATE NIGHT

Thursday 14 August
10.00pm – c11.25pm
Price Code **D**

György Ligeti
Lux aeterna   9'

Bruckner
Motets: 'Christus factus est'; 'Virga
Jesse floruit'; 'Ave Maria'   13'

Sir Harrison Birtwistle
Nenia: The Death of Orpheus*   15'

Hans Werner Henze
Orpheus Behind the Wire   17'

Ingvar Lidholm
… a riveder le stelle   12'

Swedish Radio Choir
Eric Ericson Chamber Choir
Stefan Parkman *conductor*
Claron McFadden *soprano**
Nash Ensemble

Claron McFadden

Orpheus-inspired
works by Birtwistle
and Henze (see
Season Theme,
pages 4–23) are
at the centre of a
concert in which
two outstanding
Swedish choirs bring music by a
Swedish composer with whom they
are both closely associated. Featured
composer György Ligeti's *Lux aeterna*
(familiar from *2001: A Space Odyssey*)
prefaces a trio of Bruckner motets.

PROM 37

Friday 15 August
7.30pm – c9.40pm
Price Code **A**

Mozart
Symphony No. 40 in G minor   35'

interval

Brahms
A German Requiem   65'

Miah Persson *soprano*
Peter Mattei *baritone*

Swedish Radio Choir
Eric Ericson Chamber Choir
Swedish Radio Symphony Orchestra
Manfred Honeck *conductor*

The two Swedish
choirs featured in
Prom 36 here join
the Swedish Radio
Symphony Orchestra
under its Principal
Conductor Manfred
Honeck, who has
stood in at short notice to conduct
several Proms in previous years.
Mozart's penultimate symphony was
described by Schumann as a model of
'Grecian lightness and grace', while
Brahms's monumental Requiem to texts
from the German Bible was written in
response to the deaths of both
Schumann and Brahms's mother.

Peter Mattei

💬 **6.00pm Pre-Prom Talk** (RAH)
Calum MacDonald on Brahms's Requiem

PROM 38

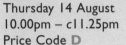
NOTE TIME

Saturday 16 August
7.00pm – c9.00pm
Price Code **A**

Great British Film Music

BBC Concert Orchestra
Rumon Gamba *conductor*

Many of Britain's leading composers
wrote film music in the great years
of British film production around the
Second World War. This celebration
presents highlights from some of the
finest of those scores, including music
by centenarian Arnold Bax for
David Lean's 1948 film *Oliver Twist*,
Alan Rawsthorne's memorable titles
for *The Cruel Sea*, Sir Malcolm Arnold's
'Comedy Suite' from *The Belles of
St Trinian's*, and Arthur Bliss's powerful
Things to Come of 1936. The story
is brought up to date with music by
leading living British film composers
Sir Richard Rodney Bennett and
John Barry.

There will be one interval

This concert will be broadcast on BBC2

PROM 39

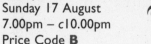

Sunday 17 August
7.00pm – c10.00pm
Price Code **B**

Berlioz
Benvenuto Cellini
(sung in French)   125'

Bruce Ford *Benvenuto Cellini*
Laura Claycomb *Teresa*
Monica Groop *Ascanio*
Christopher Maltman *Fieramosca*
Franz Hawlata *Giacomo Balducci*
Ralf Lukas *Pope Clement VII*
Johannes Chum *Francesco*
Reinhard Mayr *Bernardino*

Choir of MDR Leipzig
SWR Stuttgart Radio Symphony Orchestra
Sir Roger Norrington *conductor*

The SWR Stuttgart Radio Symphony Orchestra returns with its Principal Conductor, Sir Roger Norrington, for a rare performance (in its revised 1852 Weimar version) of bicentenary composer Hector Berlioz's early opera – a colourful, carnivalesque romp through the life and loves of Renaissance artist Benvenuto Cellini, culminating in the forging of his famous bronze statue of *Perseus with Medusa's Head* (see Berlioz, pages 30–32).

There will be two intervals

🔊 **5.30pm Pre-Prom Talk** (RAH)
Piers Burton-Page on *Benvenuto Cellini*

PROM 40

Monday 18 August
7.30pm – c9.40pm
Price Code **A**

Nielsen
Overture 'Helios'   12'

Kalevi Aho
Symphony No. 9   31'
London premiere

interval

Sibelius
The Oceanides (Yale version)   c20'
UK premiere

Symphony No. 3 in C major   29'

Christian Lindberg *trombone*

Lahti Symphony Orchestra
Osmo Vänskä *conductor*

Osmo Vänskä has won great praise for his work with his Finnish orchestra. They bring to the Proms the London premiere of fellow Finn Kalevi Aho's symphonic concerto, featuring the extraordinary trombone-playing of Christian Lindberg (see *New Music*, pages 66–75). Nielsen's sonic sunrise and a rare early version of Sibelius's watery evocation of cavorting Greek sea-nymphs (see *Season Theme*, pages 4–23) preface the great Finnish composer's Third Symphony.

🎵 **1.00pm Proms Chamber Music**
See pages 110–11

🔊 **6.00pm Pre-Prom Talk** (RAH)
Tuomas Kinberg and Mark Lowther

PROM 41

Tuesday 19 August
7.30pm – c9.30pm
Price Code **A**

Barber
Medea's Meditation and Dance
of Vengeance   12'

Chen Yi
Percussion Concerto   20'
European premiere

interval

Ravel
Daphnis and Chloë   50'

Evelyn Glennie *percussion*

BBC Symphony Chorus
BBC Symphony Orchestra
Leonard Slatkin *conductor*

Evelyn Glennie

The BBC Symphony Orchestra under its Chief Conductor Leonard Slatkin contrast two works inspired by Greek myths: Samuel Barber's reworking of music he wrote for a ballet about the vengeful witch Medea, and Ravel's classic pastoral romance about the devotees of the great god Pan (see *Season Theme*, pages 4–23). Proms favourite Evelyn Glennie is the soloist in a new Percussion Concerto written specially for her (see *New Music*, pages 66–75).

🎵 **6.00pm Composer Portrait**
Chen Yi. See page 136

PROM 42

Wednesday 20 August
7.30pm – c9.15pm
Price Code **C**

Beethoven
Overture 'The Consecration of
the House'   12'

Berlioz
La mort de Cléopâtre   22'

interval

Prokofiev
Symphonic Song   13'

Scythian Suite   20'

Olga Borodina *mezzo-soprano*

Rotterdam Philharmonic Orchestra
Valery Gergiev *conductor*

Olga Borodina

In the first of two concerts, the Rotterdam Philharmonic Orchestra and its Principal Conductor Valery Gergiev perform a pair of works by anniversary composer Sergey Prokofiev: his rarely-heard *Symphonic Song* and his blazing dance score, the *Scythian Suite* (see Prokofiev, pages 36–8). The great Russian mezzo Olga Borodina returns in Berlioz's dramatic scena (see Berlioz, pages 30–32), an early work that anticipates the tragic end of *The Trojans* (see Proms 47 & 48).

🔊 **6.00pm Pre-Prom Talk** (RAH)
David Fanning on Prokofiev

Eric Richmond/Arena Images

PROM 43

Thursday 21 August
7.30pm – c9.30pm
Price Code **C**

Ravel
Alborada del gracioso · 9'

Giya Kancheli
Warzone · c10'
UK premiere

Ravel
La valse · 12'

interval

Berlioz
Symphonie fantastique · 50'

Rotterdam Philharmonic Orchestra
Valery Gergiev *conductor*

In their second concert, Gergiev and his Rotterdam orchestra present works by two French masters of orchestral sonority: Ravel's Spanish dawn-song and nightmare vision of a Viennese waltz contrast with anniversary composer Berlioz's hallucinatory dream symphony (see *Berlioz, pages 30–32*). Kancheli's new work was composed as a 50th-birthday present for Valery Gergiev (see *New Music, pages 66–75*).

PROM 44

Friday 22 August
7.30pm – c9.25pm
Price Code **A**

Mozart
Concerto in F major
for three pianos, K242 · 20'

interval

Beethoven
Symphony No. 3 in E flat major,
'Eroica' · 50'

West-Eastern Divan Orchestra
Saleem Abboud-Ashkar *piano*
Shai Wosner *piano*
Daniel Barenboim *piano/conductor*

Daniel Barenboim

For the past five years Daniel Barenboim has dedicated himself to the creation of a unique orchestra made up of young Israeli and Arab musicians (see page 88). Fresh from this year's workshop sessions in southern Spain, they come to the UK for the first time to perform Mozart's joyful triple concerto and Beethoven's heroic Third Symphony.

🔊 **6.00pm Pre-Prom Talk** (RAH)
Daniel Barenboim and Edward Said

PROM 45

Saturday 23 August
8.00pm – c10.15pm
Price Code **A**

Musorgsky
Khovanshchina – Prelude · 5'

Shostakovich
Violin Concerto No. 1 in A minor · 38'

interval

Prokofiev
Romeo and Juliet – excerpts · 60'

Christian Tetzlaff *violin*

BBC Symphony Orchestra
Leonard Slatkin *conductor*

A leading young violinist joins the BBC Symphony Orchestra and Chief Conductor Leonard Slatkin in one of the peaks of the 20th-century violin repertoire. An all-Russian programme is completed with the dawn prelude to Musorgsky's epic opera of sectarian strife in old Moscow and highlights from anniversary composer Prokofiev's Shakespearian ballet *Romeo and Juliet* (see *Prokofiev, pages 36–8*).

This concert will be broadcast on BBC2

PROM 46

Sunday 24 August
7.00pm – c10.40pm
Price Code **B**

Handel
Saul · 159'

Neal Davies *Saul*
Andreas Scholl *David*
Mark Padmore *Jonathan*
Deborah York *Merab*
Susan Gritton *Michal*
Paul Agnew *High Priest/Witch of Endor*
Jonathan Lemalu *Ghost of Samuel*

Gabrieli Consort and Players
Paul McCreesh *conductor*

Andreas Scholl

One of Handel's most dramatic and poignant biblical oratorios is performed complete by one of our leading period ensembles. The cast is led by British bass Neal Davies as the mad king of Israel, with star German counter-tenor Andreas Scholl as his psalm-singing successor.

There will be two intervals

🔊 **5.30pm Pre-Prom Talk** (RAH)
Paul McCreesh and Ruth Smith on *Saul*

Alexandra Vosding James McMillan/Decca

PROM 47

NOTE TIME

Monday 25 August
3.00pm – c4.30pm
Price Code **C**

Berlioz
The Trojans (sung in French)
Part 1 'The Capture of Troy'   85'

Petra Lang Cassandra
Ben Heppner Aeneas
baritone TBA Corebus
Tigran Martirossian Panthus
Clive Bayley Priam
Pamela Helen Stephen Ascanius
Jonathan Lemalu Ghost of Hector
Anna Burford Hecuba
Mark Stone A Greek Captain
Leigh Melrose A Trojan Soldier
Bülent Bezdüz Helenus

London Symphony Chorus
London Symphony Orchestra
Sir Colin Davis conductor

Sir Colin Davis

No conductor has done more than Sir Colin Davis to lead the Berlioz revival of recent decades, above all in his pioneering complete performances of the composer's massive Virgilian magnum opus, The Trojans, at Covent Garden and in the recording studio in the late 1960s. A work the composer himself never heard in its entirety, it is here spread across two Proms, performed by an all-star cast (see Season Theme, pages 4–23, and Berlioz, pages 30–32).

There will be no interval

♪ **1.00pm Proms Chamber Music**
See pages 110–11

PROM 48

NOTE TIME

Monday 25 August
7.00pm – c10.20pm
Price Code **C**

Berlioz
The Trojans (sung in French)
Part 2 'The Trojans at Carthage'   153'

Michelle DeYoung Dido
Ben Heppner Aeneas
Sara Mingardo Anna
Robert Lloyd Narbal
Kenneth Tarver Iopas
Toby Spence Hylas
Tigran Martirossian Panthus
Pamela Helen Stephen Ascanius
Darren Jeffery Trojan Sentry 1
Roderick Earle Trojan Sentry 2
Petra Lang Ghost of Cassandra
baritone TBA Ghost of Corebus
Jonathan Lemalu Ghost of Hector
Clive Bayley Ghost of Priam
Leigh Melrose Mercury

London Symphony Chorus
London Symphony Orchestra
Sir Colin Davis conductor

There will be one interval

PROM 49

Tuesday 26 August
7.30pm – c9.00pm
Price Code **B**

Mahler
Symphony No. 6 in A minor   80'

European Union Youth Orchestra
Bernard Haitink conductor

Bernard Haitink

The European Union Youth Orchestra is a regular visitor to the Proms and is here reunited with one of the world's great Mahlerians for a performance of one of the composer's most compelling visions of implacable fate.

There will be no interval

PROM 50

NOTE TIME

Wednesday 27 August
7.00pm – c9.00pm
Price Code **A**

Wagner
Tannhäuser – Overture and
Venusberg Music   21'

Berg
Seven Early Songs   18'

interval

Brahms
Symphony No. 1 in C minor   45'

Christine Brewer soprano

London Philharmonic Orchestra
Mark Wigglesworth conductor

Mark Wigglesworth has established a close relationship with the London Philharmonic Orchestra at Glyndebourne, and here brings them

Christine Brewer

to the Proms in music by Wagner and Brahms, opposite poles in 19th-century German music. Christine Brewer, highly acclaimed for her singing of Wagner's Isolde with the BBC SO at the Barbican earlier this year, joins them in Berg's sensuously orchestrated set of early songs.

Clive Barda

Every Prom live on BBC Radio 3 and www.bbc.co.uk/proms

PROM 51

Wednesday 27 August
10.00pm – c11.30pm
Price Code **D**

Britten
Young Apollo   8'

Thea Musgrave
Helios – Concerto for oboe
and orchestra   17'

John Woolrich
Double Mercury   c20'
*BBC/Britten Sinfonia co-commission:
world premiere*

Stravinsky
Orpheus   30'

Paul Lewis *piano*
Nicholas Daniel *oboe*

Britten Sinfonia
Nicholas Cleobury *conductor*

Greek myths pervade this concert (see
Season Theme, pages 4–23). Apollo and
Helios were both sun-gods; Orpheus,
the musician whose song defeated
death, was Apollo's son; while Mercury
– subject of John Woolrich's new work
(see *New Music, pages 66–75*) – was
the gods' messenger to men. Britten's
brilliant 'fanfare' for piano and strings is
performed by a graduate of Radio 3's
New Generation Artists scheme, while
the soloist in Thea Musgrave's sun-filled
concerto is a past winner of BBC
Young Musicians.

There will be no interval

PROM 52

Thursday 28 August
7.30pm – c9.50pm
Price Code **A**

Nielsen
Pan and Syrinx   9'

Brahms
Violin Concerto in D major   40'

interval

Tchaikovsky
Manfred   55'

Vadim Repin *violin*

**City of Birmingham Symphony
Orchestra**
Sakari Oramo *conductor*

Vadim Repin

The Russian
virtuoso Vadim
Repin joins the
CBSO under its
Music Director
Sakari Oramo in
Brahms's popular,
gypsy-influenced
Violin Concerto. Nielsen's *Pan and
Syrinx* continues this season's survey
of Greek myths (see *pages 4–23*) and
the concert closes with a rare hearing
of Tchaikovsky's Byronic *Manfred* (see
Season Highlights, page 56).

🗨 **6.00pm Pre-Prom Talk** (RAH)
Sakari Oramo talks to Stephen Maddock

PROM 53

Friday 29 August
7.30pm – c9.20pm
Price Code **C**

Beethoven
Symphony No. 2 in D major   32'

interval

Tchaikovsky
Symphony No. 4 in F minor   43'

Pittsburgh Symphony Orchestra
Mariss Jansons *conductor*

Mariss Jansons

One of the most
exciting and
sought-after
conductors in
the world today,
who gave an
unforgettable
performance of
Dvořák's 'New World' Symphony at
last year's Proms, Mariss Jansons is
making his farewell European tour with
the Pittsburgh Symphony Orchestra,
of which he has been Music Director
since 1997. In the first of their two
Proms, they pair Beethoven's sunny
but powerful Second Symphony with
Tchaikovsky's fateful but lyrical Fourth.

PROM 54

Saturday 30 August
7.00pm – c8.55pm
Price Code **C**

Mendelssohn
Violin Concerto in E minor   26'

interval

Mahler
Symphony No. 1 in D major   55'

Gil Shaham *violin*

Pittsburgh Symphony Orchestra
Mariss Jansons *conductor*

Gil Shaham

For their second
Prom, the Pittsburgh
Symphony Orchestra
and Mariss Jansons
perform Mahler's
titanic First Symphony,
and are joined by star
Israeli-American
violinist Gil Shaham for Mendelssohn's
richly lyrical concerto.

This concert will be broadcast on BBC2

🗨 **5.30pm Pre-Prom Talk** (RAH)
Members of the Pittsburgh Symphony
Orchestra

PROM 55

Sunday 31 August
7.30pm – c9.45pm
Price Code **C**

Bartók
Music for Strings, Percussion
and Celesta   30'

György Ligeti
Violin Concerto   27'

interval

Stravinsky
The Rite of Spring   33'

Tasmin Little violin

Berliner Philharmoniker
Sir Simon Rattle conductor

The dream team of Sir Simon Rattle
and the Berliner Philharmoniker comes
to the Proms for the first time – as
does Ligeti's Violin Concerto,
performed by Tasmin Little in its
composer's 80th birthday year (see
Ligeti, pages 42–3). The concert opens
with Bartók's eerie, taut masterpiece
and closes with Stravinsky's savage,
seminal ballet, which Rattle and the
orchestra recently staged in Berlin,
danced by hundreds of schoolchildren.

This concert will be broadcast on BBC2

PROM 56

Monday 1 September
7.30pm – c9.30pm
Price Code **C**

Brahms
Variations on the St Anthony
Chorale   17'

Heiner Goebbels
Aus einem Tagebuch   24'
UK premiere

interval

R. Strauss
Ein Heldenleben   44'

Berliner Philharmoniker
Sir Simon Rattle conductor

Sir Simon Rattle

For the second of
their two Proms,
Sir Simon Rattle
and the Berlin
Philharmoniker
perform Brahms's
inventive variations
on a theme he
thought was by Haydn and Strauss's
autobiographical depiction of a hero's
life. They also introduce to the UK a
newer 'autobiographical' work by
Heiner Goebbels (see *New Music,
pages 66–75*).

♪ **1.00pm Proms Chamber Music**
See pages 110–11

💬 **6.00pm Pre-Prom Talk** (RAH)
Heiner Goebbels talks to John Tusa

PROM 57

NOTE TIME

Tuesday 2 September
7.00pm – c9.15pm
Price Code **A**

Matthias Pintscher
'en sourdine', for violin and
orchestra   23'
UK premiere

interval

Bruckner
Symphony No. 5 in B flat major   80'

Frank Peter Zimmermann violin

BBC Symphony Orchestra
Jukka-Pekka Saraste conductor

The BBC Symphony Orchestra and its
Principal Guest Conductor Jukka-Pekka
Saraste traverse the vast architectural
span of Bruckner's Fifth Symphony,
prefaced by the UK premiere of a
young German composer's violin
concerto, featuring the soloist who
gave its premiere in Berlin in February
(see *New Music, pages 66–75*).

♪ **5.30pm Composer Portrait**
Matthias Pintscher. See page 136

PROM 58

LATE NIGHT

Tuesday 2 September
10.00pm – c11.15pm
Price Code **E**

Purcell
Dido and Aeneas   64'

Sarah Connolly *Dido*
Christopher Purves *Aeneas*
Carolyn Sampson *Belinda*
D'Arcy Bleiker *Sorcerer*
Elizabeth Cragg *Second Woman*
Matthew Beale *Sailor*
Lucy Crowe *Spirit*

Choir of the Enlightenment
Orchestra of the Age
of Enlightenment
Richard Egarr director/harpsichord

Leading British
mezzo-soprano
Sarah Connolly
takes the title-role
in the last of this
season's sequence
of operas based on
the myth of the

Sarah Connolly

Trojan War and its aftermath (see
Season Theme, pages 4–23). Purcell's
taut drama portrays the tragedy of
human relationships torn apart by fate
and divine intervention. Its eloquence
speaks powerfully across the centuries.

There will be no interval

PROM 59

Wednesday 3 September
7.30pm – c9.45pm
Price Code **B**

Esa-Pekka Salonen
Insomnia   20'
UK premiere

Beethoven
Piano Concerto No. 5
in E flat major, 'Emperor'   39'

interval

Brahms
Symphony No. 2 in D major   40'

Pierre-Laurent Aimard piano

**NDR Symphony Orchestra,
Hamburg**
Christoph Eschenbach conductor

Pierre-Laurent
Aimard

The Hamburg radio orchestra last played here in one of Günter Wand's final concerts, and now returns under its Chief Conductor, Christoph Eschenbach, to perform Beethoven's Fifth Concerto with the French pianist Pierre-Laurent Aimard. The 'Emperor' is framed by Brahms's pastoral Second Symphony and Esa-Pekka Salonen's nocturnal new work (see *New Music*, pages 66–75).

PROM 60

Thursday 4 September
7.30pm – c9.35pm
Price Code **A**

Michael Berkeley
Secret Garden   16'

Bridge
Oration – Concerto elegiaco for
cello and orchestra   26'

interval

Holst
The Planets   50'

Steven Isserlis cello

BBC Singers (women's voices)
BBC National Orchestra of Wales
Richard Hickox conductor

The BBC National Orchestra of Wales and its Principal Conductor, Richard Hickox, present a pair of concerts featuring the music of Michael Berkeley – the BBC NOW's Composer in Association – and of his father, anniversary composer Lennox Berkeley. A powerful cello concerto by Frank Bridge – the teacher of Michael Berkeley's godfather, Benjamin Britten – is followed by Holst's ever-popular planetary suite.

♪ **6.00pm Composer Portrait**
Michael and Lennox Berkeley
See page 136

NOTE TIME PROM 61

Friday 5 September
7.00pm – c9.05pm
Price Code **A**

Ravel
Mother Goose – ballet   30'

Lennox Berkeley
Magnificat, Op. 71   23'

interval

Franck
Symphony in D minor   38'

**St Paul's Cathedral Choir
Westminster Abbey Choir
Westminster Cathedral Choir**

BBC National Orchestra of Wales
Richard Hickox conductor

In their second Prom, the BBC NOW and Richard Hickox are joined by the three London cathedral choirs that gave the first performance of the *Magnificat* that Lennox Berkeley wrote for the opening of the 1968 City of London Festival. It is framed by Ravel's exquisite fairy-tale ballet and Franck's only symphony, which still remains remarkable for its unity of themes across the work.

LATE NIGHT PROM 62

Friday 5 September
10.00pm – c11.20pm
Price Code **D**

Isaac
Angeli archangeli   7'

Busnoys
Fortuna desperata   2'

Josquin des Prez
Missa Fortuna desperata   22'
interspersed with

Robert Saxton
Five Motets   c24'
BBC commission: world premiere

Tye and **Byrd**
'In nomine' settings   6'

Josquin des Prez
Illibata Dei virgo nutrix   7'

**The Clerks' Group
His Majestys Sagbutts and Cornetts**
Edward Wickham director

Josquin's *Missa Fortuna desperata* is prefaced by the Busnoys motet on which it is based and interspersed with 'In nomine' settings by 16th-century English composers and a brand-new set of motets commissioned from Robert Saxton in his 50th birthday year (see *New Music*, pages 66–75).

There will be no interval

PROM 63

Saturday 6 September
6.30pm – c10.20pm
Price Code **B**

Prokofiev
War and Peace
(sung in English; semi-staged)   200'

Cast includes:
Simon Keenlyside Andrey
Catrin Wyn-Davies Natasha
John Daszak Pierre
Willard W. White Kutuzov
Peter Sidhom Napoleon
Catherine Wyn-Rogers Akhrosimova
Andrew Shore Denisov
Gwynne Howell Bolkonsky
John Graham-Hall Anatole
Clive Bayley Dolokhov

**Chorus and Orchestra of
English National Opera
Paul Daniel** conductor

English National Opera marks the
Prokofiev anniversary (see pages 36–8)
by reuniting many of the cast from
Tim Albery's critically acclaimed 2001
production of the composer's operatic
masterpiece. Based on Tolstoy's many-
peopled canvas of Russian society
before, during and after the
Napoleonic invasion, it was never
staged complete in Prokofiev's lifetime.

There will be one interval

🔊 **5.00pm Pre-Prom Talk** (RAH)
David Nice on War and Peace

PROM 64

Sunday 7 September
4.30pm – c6.30pm
Price Code **C**

Prokofiev
Symphony No. 1 in D major,
'Classical'   15'

Vivaldi, arr. McFerrin
Concerto in G minor for two cellos,
RV 531   10'

Mozart
Symphony No. 25 in G minor   24'

interval

Dukas
The Sorcerer's Apprentice   12'

Ravel
Boléro   16'

Tamás Várga cello
**Vienna Philharmonic Orchestra
Bobby McFerrin** vocalist/conductor

Bobby McFerrin

One of the world's
greatest orchestras
takes a new
direction and visits
the Proms for a
popular programme
under the baton of
one of the world's
most original musicians, who not only
conducts but sings one of the two cello
parts in his own unique arrangement of
a Vivaldi double concerto. Truly a
concert for all the family.

PROM 65

Sunday 7 September
8.00pm – c9.55pm
Price Code **A**

Donatoni
Prom   15'

Britten
Phaedra*   15'

interval

Stravinsky
Oedipus rex
(sung in Latin with English narration) 50'

Lorraine Hunt Lieberson
mezzo-soprano*/Jocasta
Robert Gambill Oedipus
Edgaras Montvidas Shepherd
Jan-Hendrik Rootering
Creon/Messenger
Juha Uusitalo Tiresias

BBC Singers (men's voices)
**BBC Symphony Orchestra
Jukka-Pekka Saraste** conductor

The leading American mezzo Lorraine
Hunt Lieberson stars in two great
20th-century works based on classic
Greek myths of incestuous passion (see
Season Theme, pages 4–23). The late
Franco Donatoni's Prom, posthumously
premiered by the BBC Symphony
Orchestra at the Barbican, finally arrives
at the venue the composer intended.

🔊 **6.30pm Pre-Prom Talk** (RCM)
Stephen Johnson on Oedipus rex

PROM 66

Monday 8 September
7.00pm – c9.05pm
Price Code **A**

Prokofiev
Piano Concerto No. 1
in D flat major   15'

interval

Shostakovich
Symphony No. 7 in C major,
'Leningrad'   79'

Nikolai Lugansky piano

**Royal Scottish National Orchestra
Alexander Lazarev** conductor

Nikolai Lugansky

The Royal Scottish
National Orchestra
and its Principal
Conductor
Alexander Lazarev
mark the 300th
anniversary of the
founding of the city
of St Petersburg with a performance
of the massive symphony that
Shostakovich famously wrote there
during the German siege of 1941.
Tchaikovsky Competition winner
Nikolai Lugansky is the soloist in
the popular First Piano Concerto by
anniversary composer Prokofiev (see
pages 36–8).

🎵 **1.00pm Proms Chamber Music**
See pages 110–11

LATE NIGHT — PROM 67

Monday 8 September
10.00pm – c11.30pm
Price Code **D**

Xenakis
Nuits   9'

Idmen A & B   28'
UK premiere

Cage
Third Construction   10'

James Wood
Tongues of Fire   22'
world premiere

**New London Chamber Choir
Amadinda Percussion Ensemble.
James Wood** *conductor*

Composer, conductor and instrument-inventor James Wood conducts his specialist British choir and Hungary's leading percussion group in his own new work (*see New Music, pages 66–75*), prefaced by Cage's percussion classic and two works by the late Iannis Xenakis: *Idmen*, his elemental evocation of an ancient Greek creation myth (*see pages 4–23*), which will involve some audience participation, and *Nuits*, an unaccompanied choral work dedicated to 'unknown political prisoners' everywhere.

PROM 68

Tuesday 9 September
7.30pm – c9.45pm
Price Code **C**

Stravinsky
Symphony in Three Movements   22'

Rimsky-Korsakov
Sheherazade   42'

interval

Stravinsky
Petrushka   34'

**Israel Philharmonic Orchestra
Zubin Mehta** *conductor*

The Israel Philharmonic Orchestra makes a long-awaited return to the Proms under its Music Director for Life in a programme celebrating the exotic colours of Russia. Stravinsky's ground-breaking Diaghilev ballet and the wartime symphony he composed in America frame the exotic *Arabian Nights* suite composed by his teacher, Rimsky-Korsakov.

NOTE TIME — PROM 69

Wednesday 10 September
7.00pm – c9.10pm
Price Code **A**

Prokofiev
The Stone Flower – excerpts   10'

Beethoven
Piano Concerto No. 4 in G major   34'

interval

Mahler
Symphony No. 4 in G major   54'

Christian Blackshaw *piano*
Rebecca Evans *soprano*

**BBC Philharmonic
Gianandrea Noseda** *conductor*

Gianandrea Noseda

The BBC Philharmonic and its Principal Conductor Gianandrea Noseda offer a rare chance to hear music from Prokofiev's final ballet. Christian Blackshaw is the pianist in a Beethoven concerto whose second movement is widely thought to evoke the myth of Orpheus. And Rebecca Evans joins the orchestra in the child's-eye vision of heaven that closes Mahler's radiant Fourth Symphony.

🔊 **5.15pm Audience Forum**
(RAH) Nicholas Kenyon & David Elliott

LATE NIGHT — PROM 70

Wednesday 10 September
10.00pm – c11.30pm
Price Code **E**

Bach
Cantata No. 170, 'Vergnügte Ruh,
beliebte Seelenlust'   24'

Rameau
Dances from 'Les Indes galantes', 'Platée',
'Dardanus' and 'Les Boréades'   30'

Handel
Ariodante – 'Scherza infida';
'Dopo notte'   16'

Anne Sofie von Otter *mezzo-soprano*

**Les Musiciens du Louvre – Grenoble
Marc Minkowski** *conductor*

Anne Sofie von Otter

The world-renowned mezzo Anne Sofie von Otter joins French conductor Marc Minkowski and his period-instrument players in a pair of arias from Handel's great opera *Ariodante* and one of Bach's most richly scored cantatas. Of the four operas from which the selection of dazzling dances by Rameau is drawn, three are based on Greek myths (*see Season Theme, pages 4–23*).

PROM 71

Thursday 11 September
7.30pm – c9.25pm
Price Code **C**

R. Strauss
Don Juan   17'

Elgar
Cello Concerto in E minor   28'

interval

Musorgsky, orch. Ravel
Pictures at an Exhibition   32'

Yo-Yo Ma *cello*

Tonhalle Orchestra, Zürich
David Zinman *conductor*

Yo-Yo Ma

The Zürich Tonhalle Orchestra and its American Music Director David Zinman have recently embarked on a complete recorded cycle of the orchestral works of Strauss. The famous Chinese-American cellist Yo-Yo Ma joins them for his first Proms performance of the greatest British cello concerto. And the concert ends with Musorgsky's pianistic picture gallery, as expanded into an orchestral showpiece by Ravel.

PROM 72

Friday 12 September
7.30pm – c9.45pm
Price Code **B**

Sir Harrison Birtwistle
The Shadow of Night   30'
UK premiere

interval

Beethoven
Symphony No. 9 in D minor,
'Choral'   70'

Diana Damrau *soprano*
Charlotte Hellekant *mezzo-soprano*
Robert Dean Smith *tenor*
Alastair Miles *bass*

Geoffrey Mitchell Choir
Philharmonia Chorus
Philharmonia Orchestra
Christoph von Dohnányi *conductor*

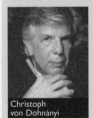
Christoph von Dohnányi

The mood swings from dark to light as Sir Harrison Birtwistle's new Dürer- and Dowland-inspired orchestral meditation on melancholy (see *New Music*, pages 66–75) provides the prelude to the annual Proms performance of Beethoven's life-affirming Ninth Symphony, with its final choral setting of Schiller's 'Ode to Joy'.

💬 **6.00pm Pre-Prom Talk** (RAH)
Sir Harrison Birtwistle talks to Jonathan Cross

PROM 73

NOTE TIME

Saturday 13 September
7.45pm – c10.45pm
Price Code **F**

THE LAST NIGHT OF THE PROMS 2003

Berlioz
Overture 'Roman Carnival'   8'

Saint-Saëns
Introduction and Rondo
capriccioso   10'

Fauré
Pavane   7'

Joseph Phibbs
new work   c10'
BBC commission: world premiere

Catalani
La Wally – 'Ebben? Ne andrò
lontana'   4'

Gounod
Faust – 'O Dieu! Que de bijoux!'
(Jewel Song)   5'

Leoncavallo
Pagliacci – 'Stridono lassù'   3'

interval

Vaughan Williams
The Wasps – Overture   9'

Borodin
Prince Igor – Polovtsian Dances   12'

Massenet
Thaïs – Méditation   5'

Bizet
Carmen – 'L'amour est un oiseau
rebelle' (Habanera)   4'

Teodor Grigoriu
Valurile Dunării – 'Muzica'   3'

Elgar
Pomp and Circumstance
March No. 1   5'

Wood & Grainger,
arr. John Wilson
Fantasia on British Sea-Songs   19'

Parry, orch. Elgar
Jerusalem   2'

The National Anthem   2'

Auld Lang Syne   1'

Angela Gheorghiu *soprano*
Leila Josefowicz *violin*

BBC Singers
BBC Symphony Chorus
BBC Symphony Orchestra
Leonard Slatkin *conductor*

Two international stars join the British traditions of the Last Night. As Fauré bids farewell to a mythical Greece, Borodin's exotic dances and a newly commissioned work usher in the

Angela Gheorghiu

festivities around the country (see *opposite page*).

This concert will be broadcast on BBC2 (Part 1) and BBC1 (Part 2)

1 Henry Fair Terry O'Neill/Decca Sasha Gusov

PROMS in the Park

The BBC presents the eighth season of Proms in the Park, bringing the atmosphere of the Last Night of the Proms simultaneously to audiences in England, Ireland, Scotland and Wales for the very first time, during a closing weekend that features appearances by all five of the BBC's orchestras. All four Proms in the Park events culminate in live big-screen link-ups with the Royal Albert Hall.

BBC Proms in the Park continues to be a colourful conclusion to the season's programme, attracting capacity audiences to outdoor venues across the country, with all events sponsored by Renault. This year's concerts are broadcast across BBC Radio and Television: BBC Radio 2 broadcasts from Hyde Park, and BBC Radio Ulster, Scotland and Wales broadcast their local events. Highlights of all four Proms in the Park will be televised as part of the coverage of the Last Night on BBC1 and BBC2, while Digital Satellite and Freeview viewers can watch the first half of the Hyde Park event on BBC2.

Events sponsored by RENAULT

BBC Proms in the Park, London

Bass-baritone Bryn Terfel, musical star Ruthie Henshall and pianist Jean-Yves Thibaudet lead the celebrity line-up joining the BBC Concert Orchestra under Robin Stapleton for the main part of the evening's entertainment in Hyde Park, hosted once again by Terry Wogan.

THE ROYAL PARKS

Saturday 13 September

Hyde Park. Gates open 4.00pm; entertainment on stage from 5.30pm

Tickets: £18.00 (under-3s free), available now by post/fax using the Booking Form facing page 122, by phone on 0870 899 8100 (24 hours, national rate) or online via www.bbc.co.uk/proms, and also (after 16 June) from the Royal Albert Hall on 020 7589 8212 (9.00am–9.00pm). A £2.00 transaction fee applies.

Corporate hospitality facilities are available. Call Charles Webb on 01484 435 569.

BBC Proms in the Park, Belfast

Northern Ireland joins the Last Night festivities for the second time following the success of the first Belfast Prom in the Park last year. Live open-air concert in the grounds of City Hall in Belfast's Donegall Square, with the Ulster Orchestra.

Saturday 13 September

Donegall Square, Belfast.
Tickets: To apply for free tickets, please send a stamped addressed envelope to: Proms in the Park, Ticket Unit, BBC Broadcasting House, Ormeau Avenue, Belfast BT2 8HQ.

BBC Proms in the Park, Glasgow

The BBC Scottish Symphony Orchestra performs in Scotland's first Prom in the Park at Glasgow's Pacific Quay.

Saturday 13 September

Pacific Quay, Glasgow.
Tickets: £7.50. Available by phone from the Glasgow Science Centre on 0141 420 5005

BBC Proms in the Park, Swansea

Proms in the Park returns to Swansea's Singleton Park for a concert featuring Welsh tenor Robert Tear, Swansea-born actor-singer Steve Balsamo and Royal Harpist Catrin Finch with the BBC National Orchestra of Wales under conductor Peter Stark.

Saturday 13 September

Singleton Park, Swansea.
Tickets: £6.50 in advance or £8.00 on the day (under-12s free), from the BBC Call NOW line on 0870 013 1812 or the Grand Theatre Box Office on 01792 475 715, or in person from the Grand Theatre Box Office, Singleton Street, Swansea.

Note that all BBC Proms in the Park events are outdoors and tickets are unreserved. The use of chairs is discouraged since it obstructs the view of others, but if you find it necessary because of limited mobility, please be considerate to your neighbours. In the interest of safety, please do not bring glass items, barbecues or flaming torches.

Tickets for both BBC Proms in the Park, London, and the CBBC Prom in the Park can also be bought in person (no transaction fee) at the BBC Shops at 50 Margaret Street, London W1, and Bush House, The Strand, London WC2

CBBC Prom in the Park, London

The Hyde Park celebrations don't end with the Last Night on Saturday evening! The weekend's music party continues on Sunday afternoon with the popular CBBC Prom in the Park, a wonderful celebration of music for children and families, presented by CBBC's Angellica Bell and Matt Baker, and featuring the musicians of the BBC Philharmonic (conductor Philip Ellis) alongside top acts from the charts and favourite stars from CBBC programmes.

Sunday 14 September

Hyde Park. Gates open 1.00pm; entertainment on stage from 2.30pm

Tickets: £12.00 (adults), £7.50 (children 3–16, under-3s free), available now by post/fax using the Booking Form facing page 122, by phone on 0870 899 8001 (24 hours, national rate) or online via www.bbc.co.uk/proms, and also (after 16 June) from the Royal Albert Hall on 020 7589 8212 (9.00am–9.00pm). A £2.00 transaction fee applies.

Proms Chamber Music

Mondays at 1.00pm
Lecture Theatre, Victoria & Albert Museum
Broadcast live on BBC Radio 3
and repeated the following Sunday at 1.00pm

Christopher Cook

The BBC Proms and the Victoria & Albert Museum continue their popular collaboration, presenting eight Monday-lunchtime concerts highlighting Proms artists, themes and anniversaries in the intimate setting of the Lecture Theatre at the V&A, a short walk from the Royal Albert Hall.

Hosted by Christopher Cook

Note that admission to the V&A is free and that the museum and its restaurant are open daily from 10.00am.

How to Book
All tickets £6.00.
Advance booking is advised.

Before the day of the **concert** all bookings should be made with the Royal Albert Hall Box Office, *either* using the priority Booking Form *(facing page 122)*, the Online Ticket Request system (at www.bbc.co.uk/proms) *or* by telephone or in person (from Monday 16 June).

On the day of the concert tickets can only be bought *(subject to availability)* at the V&A, Exhibition Road entrance *(see map, page 114)*.

PCM 1

Monday 21 July
1.00pm – c2.00pm

György Ligeti
Six Bagatelles   11'

Debussy
Syrinx   3'

Britten
Six Metamorphoses
after Ovid   14'

Farkas
Old Hungarian Dances
of the 17th Century   10'

György Ligeti
Ten Pieces   13'

Galliard Ensemble
Kathryn Thomas *flute*
Owen Dennis *oboe*
Katherine Spencer *clarinet*
Richard Bayliss *horn*
Helen Simons *bassoon*

A sparkling start to the Proms Chamber Music series with a youthful ensemble of Radio 3 New Generation Artists celebrating Ligeti's 80th birthday year with two quintets that explore the myriad possibilities of woodwind colour and virtuosity. Music by Ligeti's teacher and two haunting works on the Proms theme of Greek myths complete this varied programme.

PCM 2

Monday 28 July
1.00pm – c2.00pm

John Corigliano
Fantasia on an Ostinato   12'

Beethoven
Piano Sonata in D minor,
Op. 31 No. 2,
'The Tempest'   23'

Bach, arr. Busoni
Chaconne (from Partita,
BWV 1004)   15'

Hélène Grimaud *piano*

The day after her Proms appearance playing Bartók's Concerto No. 3 (Prom 13), this brilliant French pianist gives a fascinatingly unusual solo recital. Corigliano takes an idea from Beethoven for a compelling keyboard meditation that complements Beethoven's own radical 'Tempest' Sonata and Busoni's re-creation of Bach's tautly dramatic Chaconne.

Hélène Grimaud

PCM 3

Monday 4 August
1.00pm – c2.00pm

György Ligeti
Horn Trio   22'

Brahms
Horn Trio   28'

David Pyatt *horn*
Gordan Nikolitch *violin*
Leon McCawley *piano*

Further evidence of how Ligeti's quicksilver art transforms all that it touches in his kaleidoscopic Horn Trio, played by an ensemble unrivalled in this repertoire. Subtitled 'Hommage à Brahms', Ligeti's work is paired with its gloriously romantic forerunner, which inspired it at least in spirit: 'it floats in the celestial spheres of the musical heavens'.

PCM 4

Monday 11 August
1.00pm – c2.00pm

Haydn
Arianna a Naxos   17'

Judith Weir
The Voice of Desire   c10'
BBC commission: world premiere

Wolf
Songs, including 'Denk es, o
Seele!' and 'Verborgenheit'   10'

R. Strauss
Songs, including 'Die Nacht'
and 'Morgen'   10'

Alice Coote *mezzo-soprano*
Julius Drake *piano*

The premiere of a major new
commission from one of
Britain's leading composers,
whose musical imagination
works its magic on English
and Yoruba texts for the
unique voice of this Radio 3
New Generation Artist. Greek
myth provides the subject for
Haydn's impassioned cantata,
and the centenary of master
songwriter Hugo Wolf is
also celebrated.

Alice Coote

PCM 5

Monday 18 August
1.00pm – c2.00pm

Monte
Missa sine nomine   27'

Byrd
Quomodo cantabimus   8'

Lassus
Timor et tremor   5'

Monte
O bone Jesu   8'

The Tallis Scholars
Peter Phillips *director*

A newly rediscovered late-
Renaissance mass is brought
vividly to life by an acclaimed
vocal group. Filippo di Monte,
court composer to the
Habsburg dynasty and
dubbed a 'Prince of Music' by
his contemporaries, died 400
years ago and is placed here
in the company of two of his
illustrious and innovative
contemporaries.

PCM 6

Monday 25 August
1.00pm – c2.00pm

Wolf
Italian Serenade   7'

Beethoven
String Quartet in F minor,
Op. 95, 'Serioso'   19'

Lutoslawski
String Quartet   25'

**Karol Szymanowski
Quartet**
Marek Dumicz *violin*
Grzegorz Kotow *violin*
Vladimir Mykitka *viola*
Marcin Sieniawski *cello*

Another aspect of Wolf's
genius emerges in this
concert's opening work,
played by prize-winning
Radio 3 New Generation
Artists. Beethoven's
concentrated, at times
hallucinatory, quartet is the
perfect foil for Lutoslawski's
urgent and elusive music,
included in homage to a
composer who would have
been 90 this year.

PCM 7

Monday 1 September
1.00pm – c2.00pm

Prokofiev
Cello Sonata, Op. 119   22'

Robert Saxton
Sonata for Solo Cello
on a Theme of
Sir William Walton   10'
London premiere

Poulenc
Cello Sonata   22'

Steven Isserlis *cello*
Kirill Gerstein *piano*

The death of Prokofiev 50
years ago is marked with his
brooding and lyrical Sonata
played by a leading cellist.
The final version of Poulenc's

Steven Isserlis

ebullient and
poignant
Sonata dates
from the
same year,
1953, which
also saw the
birth of Robert Saxton, who
describes his work, premiered
in Aldeburgh in 2000, as 'a
voyage of discovery in search
of Walton's melody'.

PCM 8

Monday 8 September
1.00pm – c2.00pm

Berlioz
La mort d'Orphée –
Monologue and Larghetto   9'

The Damnation of Faust –
excerpts   18'

Romeo and Juliet –
excerpts   20'

Ensemble Carpe Diem
Françoise Masset *soprano*
Catherine Montier *violin*
Antoine Tamestit *viola*
Emmanuelle Bertrand *cello*
Jérôme Bertrand *double bass*
Adeline de Preissac *harp*
Marine Perez *flute*
Jean-Pierre Arnaud *oboe*
Philippe Bréas *horn*

A Proms debut for a lively
chamber group from France.
Specialising in original
transcriptions, these young
musicians bring a special
Berlioz bicentenary
programme to close the
Proms Chamber Music series
with a flourish, including a
final classical myth in heroic
style – very appropriate from
a maverick composer who
both confounded and
delighted his audiences!

Special Offers

You can claim any of these discounts when booking

By post or fax using the Priority Booking Form facing page 122

By phone or in person (*from Monday 16 June*), mentioning the relevant offer

Online (*except for Proms Odyssey*) by visiting the Proms website: www.bbc.co.uk/proms

All offers are subject to availability. Offers and discounts may not be combined.

Proms Odyssey

Immerse yourself in this year's theme of Greek myths and travel through the season using the Proms Odyssey offer. By booking for three concerts or more from the list below, you can enjoy discounted tickets as well as having a tremendous musical experience.

Save 20% when you book for three concerts, 25% on four concerts and 30% on five or more concerts – plus you will receive a free programme voucher for each concert you book for.

The Odyssey offer applies to Centre/Side Stalls and Front/Rear Circle seating areas and the same number of tickets must be booked for each concert in each area. This offer cannot be booked online. Offer closes 4 July.

PROM 3
Sunday 20 July, 7.00pm
Tippett *King Priam*

PROM 8
Wednesday 23 July, 10.00pm
Mendelssohn *Antigone*

PROM 15
Tuesday 29 July, 7.00pm
Strauss *Elektra*

PROM 30
Sunday 10 August, 7.30pm
Stravinsky *Perséphone*

PROM 41
Tuesday 19 August, 7.30pm
Ravel *Daphnis and Chloë*

PROM 47
Monday 25 August, 3.00pm
Berlioz *The Trojans – Part 1 'The Capture of Troy'*

PROM 48
Monday 25 August, 7.00pm
Berlioz *The Trojans – Part 2 'The Trojans at Carthage'*

Please note that *The Trojans* counts as two concerts.

PROM 58
Tuesday 2 September, 10.00pm
Purcell *Dido and Aeneas*

PROM 65
Sunday 7 September, 8.00pm
Stravinsky *Oedipus rex*

See listings pages for full programme details.

Group Bookings

Groups of 10 or more can claim a 10% discount on the price of Centre/Side Stalls or Front/Rear Circle tickets for all Proms in the A, B, D and E price bands, and a 5% discount for C band concerts. The offer does not apply to F and G band concerts. Look out for the 'G' symbol on the Listings pages and Priority Booking Form.

For more information, call the Group Booking Information Line: 020 7838 3108. Please note that for security reasons group purchases can only be made online during the Priority Booking period. This offer is subject to availability.

Same Day Savers

Book for more than one concert on the same day, and save £4.00 on your ticket for the later concert.

Note: Offer applies to matinée, evening and late night performances in the Royal Albert Hall. Not valid for Arena, Gallery and Circle (Restricted View) price areas.

Weekend Promming Pass

Beat the queues at the weekend and save money! In addition to discounted tickets, the Weekend Promming Pass offers guaranteed access up to 10 minutes before start-time to the Arena or Gallery standing areas for all concerts in the Royal Albert Hall on Fridays, Saturdays and Sundays (excluding Proms 72 and 73). Passes can be purchased in advance – by post or fax (using the Priority Booking Form) and online, and by phone (from 16 June) – or in person at the Box Office up to 6.00pm on Friday nights (5.30pm on 8 August and 5 September). Prices vary for each weekend depending on the number of concerts. Note that Weekend 2 excludes the *Blue Peter* Prom; Weekend 6 includes Bank Holiday Monday (25 August); and there is no pass covering Proms 72 and 73.

Passes are non-transferable and signature ID may be requested upon entry. Purchase of a Weekend Pass does not guarantee entry to the Last Night, but tickets may be counted towards the 'Six Concert Rule' (see page 119) in conjunction with further Passes or Day Ticket stubs.

Note that you may purchase a maximum of four passes per weekend (subject to availability).

Weekend Promming Pass prices

Weekend 1	Proms 1–3	£10
Weekend 2	Proms 10, 12 & 13	£10
Weekend 3	Proms 19–22	£14
Weekend 4	Proms 27–30	£14
Weekend 5	Proms 37–39	£10
Weekend 6	Proms 44–48	£18
Weekend 7	Proms 53–55	£10
Weekend 8	Proms 61–65	£18

Under-16s

The Proms are a great way to discover live music, and we encourage anyone over 5 years old to attend. Tickets for Under-16s can be purchased at half-price in any seating area for the following Proms. The *Blue Peter* Prom (Prom 11) is expressly designed to introduce children to concert-going, while the other concerts have been highlighted because they include music that will appeal to the younger audience.

PROM 2
The Nation's Favourite Prom, including Prokofiev's *Peter & the Wolf* narrated by Sir David Attenborough.

PROM 6
A celebration of the 350th anniversary of Corelli.

PROM 11
Blue Peter Prom: a concert on the theme of Magical Journeys with presenters Konnie Huq and Simon Thomas.

PROM 17
The Young Person's Guide to the Orchestra rounds off a 'royal command performance' by Sir Andrew Davis and the BBC Symphony Orchestra.

PROM 20
Former Vienna Boys' Choir member HK Gruber conducts his own *Dancing in the Dark*, Vassily Sinaisky conducts Prokofiev's most popular piano concerto and Tchaikovsky's fateful Fifth Symphony.

PROM 22
The youthful Mahler Chamber Orchestra performs Ravel, Mozart and Mendelssohn's 'Scottish' Symphony.

PROM 25
Virtuoso trumpeter Håkan Hardenberger joins the National Youth Orchestra of Scotland and Martyn Brabbins.

PROM 29
The National Youth Orchestra of Great Britain plays Berlioz's *Harold in Italy* (with viola-player Lawrence Power) and Prokofiev's awesome Fifth Symphony.

PROM 38
Film music favourites by British composers from Arnold Bax to Richard Rodney Bennett.

PROM 40
Sensational trombonist Christian Lindberg in a concert that includes Sibelius's Third Symphony.

PROM 41
Evelyn Glennie performs Chen Yi's Percussion Concerto in a concert including the radiant *Daphnis and Chloë* by Ravel.

PROM 49
Mahler's monumental Sixth Symphony with the European Union Youth Orchestra.

PROM 64
Bobby McFerrin and the Vienna Philharmonic perform *The Sorcerer's Apprentice* and Ravel's *Boléro*.

For information on Season Tickets, see page 118.

Getting to the Royal Albert Hall (and other Proms venues)

The following buses stop where indicated:

No. 9 to Charing Cross
No. 10 to Euston and King's Cross
No. 52 to Victoria

No. 9 to Hammersmith
No. 10 to Hammersmith
No. 52 to Notting Hill and Willesden

(all these buses operate as Night Buses after midnight)

No. 360 to/from Elephant & Castle

Please note that the Royal Albert Hall lies outside the Congestion Charging Zone

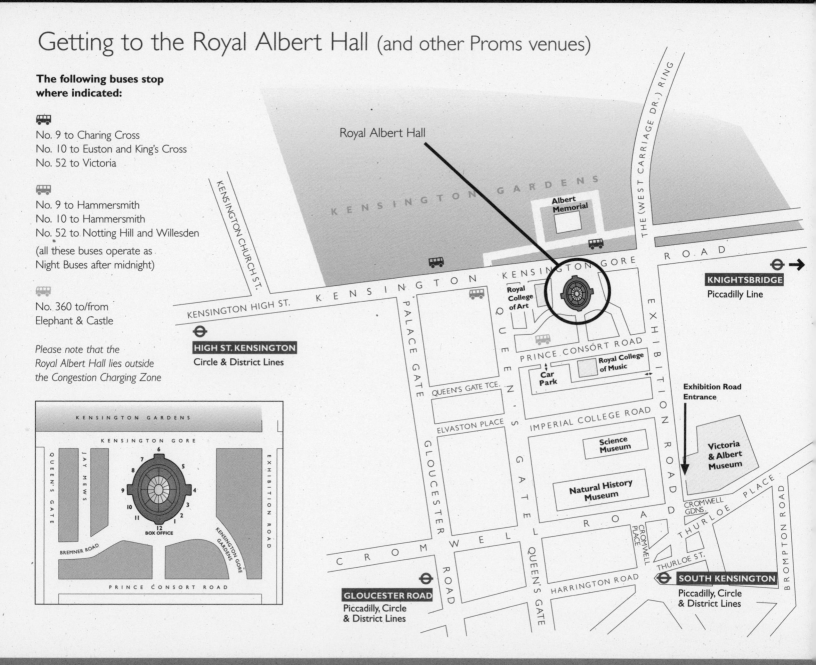

Royal Albert Hall

Every Prom live on BBC Radio 3 and www.bbc.co.uk/proms

At the Royal Albert Hall

Doors open 45 minutes before each concert (earlier for restaurant access).

Latecomers will not be admitted into the auditorium until there is a suitable break in the music. There is a video monitor with digital audio relay in the foyer at Door 6.

Bags and coats may be left in the cloakrooms at Door 4 (ground level), Door 8 (circle level) and at basement level. Folding chairs and hand-luggage larger than a briefcase are not allowed in the auditorium.

Dos and Don'ts Eating, drinking and smoking are not permitted inside the auditorium, and the use of cameras, video cameras and recording equipment is strictly forbidden. Mobile phones and watch alarms must be turned off.

Children under 5 In consideration of our audience and artists, children under the age of 5 are not allowed in the auditorium. Children between the ages of 5 and 16 are positively encouraged (see Special Offers, pages 112–113).

Car Parking A limited number of parking spaces are available from 6.00pm in the Imperial College Car Park (Prince Consort or Exhibition Road entrances). These can be booked in advance (priced £7.50) by ticking the appropriate column on the Priority Booking Form (facing page 122) or by telephoning the Box Office (open 9.00am–9.00pm daily, from 16 June) on 020 7589 8212. Please note that, if attending both early-evening and late-night concerts, only one parking fee is payable.

Dress Code There is no dress code at the Proms.

Notice Boards Notice boards with Proms news and programme and artist updates are located around the Hall.

Eating and drinking at the RAH

Restaurants The Royal Albert Hall has three restaurants catering for all tastes, from light meals to three-course dinners.

Pre-concert refreshments
All restaurants open two hours before the start of the performance.

The Elgar Restaurant offers a three-course menu with full table service. Tables in the Elgar Restaurant are bookable in advance on 020 7838 3101. Enter via Door 8 to the Circle level.

The Café Consort offers a full menu including salads, sandwiches and light meals. Enter via Door 12 to the Grand Tier level.

The Victoria Brasserie is a self-service restaurant offering a range of light meals, salads and desserts. Enter via Door 2 to the Circle level.

Post-concert drinks and light meals are available in the Café Consort after main evening concerts.

Catering in your box
Box hospitality can be pre-ordered by telephoning 020 7589 5666. Please allow two working days' notice.

Bars are located on every floor and all offer a full range of alcoholic and soft drinks, hot beverages, ice cream, confectionery and sandwiches.

The Champagne and North Circle Bars open two hours before the start of the performance, offering a range of sandwiches. A small amount of seating is available. Enter via Door 2 to the Grand Tier and Circle level respectively.

The following bars open 45 minutes before the start of the performance:

Lanson Arena Bar is located in the Arena Foyers, sub-basement level – enter via Door 2.

Door 6 and 7 Bars are located at ground level – enter via Door 6.

The Porch Bars are located at ground level – enter via Door 4 or 9.

The Grand Tier Bars are located at Grand Tier level – enter via Door 4 or 9.

The Second Tier Bar is located at Second Tier level – entrer via Door 4.

Please note that you are not permitted to consume your own food and drink in the Hall. In the interests of Health & Safety, glasses and bottles are not allowed in the auditorium except as part of box hospitality ordered through the Hall's caterers.

Information for disabled concert-goers

Access at the Proms

Call the **Access Information Line** on **020 7838 3110** for advice on facilities for disabled concert-goers (including car parking) at all Proms venues; if you have any special requirements; or to request a Royal Albert Hall Access leaflet. Dedicated staff will be available from 9.00am to 9.00pm, seven days a week. The Access leaflet is also available from the RAH website – www.royalalberthall.com.

Wheelchair access is available at all Proms venues, but advance booking is advised.

The Royal Albert Hall has up to 14 spaces bookable in the Stalls for wheelchair-users and their companions (entrance via Door 8). End-of-aisle places are priced as Centre Stalls seats; front-row platform spaces either side of the stage are priced as Side Stalls seats; rear platform places are priced as Front Circle seats. There are now also up to six spaces in the Front Circle, priced as such. When filling in the Booking Form, tick your preferred price range (ie Centre Stalls, Side Stalls or Front Circle) and enter the number of places required under the 'Wheelchair space' column.

For other Proms venues, spaces can be reserved by calling **020 7838 3110**.

Passenger lifts at the Royal Albert Hall are located off the ground-floor corridor at Doors 2, 8 and 11.

Booking

Disabled concert-goers (and a companion) receive a 50% discount on all ticket prices (except Arena and Gallery areas) for concerts at the Royal Albert Hall and for Proms Chamber Music concerts at the V&A. To claim this discount, tick the 'Disabled' box at the end of the Booking Form, or call the Access Information Line on **020 7838 3110** if booking by phone (from Monday 16 June).

The Royal Albert Hall has an infra-red system with a number of personal receivers for use with and without hearing aids. To make use of the service, collect a free receiver from the Door 6 Information Desk.

If you have a guide dog, the best place to sit in the Royal Albert Hall is in a Loggia or Second Tier Box, where your dog may stay with you. If you are sitting elsewhere, stewards will be happy to look after your dog while you enjoy the concert. Please call the Access Information Line on **020 7838 3110** to organise in advance of your visit.

Proms Guide: non-print versions

An audio cassette version of this *Guide* is available in two parts, 'Concert Listings' and 'Articles' (£2.50 each, £5 for both). Order on 020 7765 3260.

Braille and computer disc versions of this *Guide* are available in two parts, 'Concert Listings' and 'Articles' (£2.50 each, £5 for both). Order from RNIB Customer Services: 0845 7023 153.

Radio 3 commentary

Visually impaired patrons are welcome to use the free infra-red hearing facility (*see above*) to listen in to the broadcast commentary on Radio 3.

Programme-reading service

Ask at the Door 6 Information Desk if you would like a steward to read your programme out to you.

Large-print programmes & texts

Large-print concert programmes can be made available on the night (at the same price as the standard programme) if ordered not less than five working days in advance. Complimentary large-print texts and opera librettos can also be made available on the night (where applicable) if ordered in advance. To order any large-print programmes or texts, please telephone 020 7765 3260. They will be left for collection at the Door 6 Information Desk 45 minutes before the start of the concert.

Royal Albert Hall Development Update

Regular Prom-goers will already be aware of the building development in progress at the Royal Albert Hall. The Hall is almost at the end of a £70 million programme, due for completion in December 2003.

2003 is the final year of the building development programme. Audiences have benefited already from the extensive improvements to the front-of-house areas, especially the two new Arena Foyers and the introduction of fresh air ventilation to the auditorium. The final stages of the work include:

The South Porch
The new South Porch will be open to the public in time for the Proms. It will provide a daytime entrance to the Hall, giving access to the Box Office, and will lead to a much improved and enlarged public restaurant at first floor level. From 2004 the Hall will be offering regular accompanied tours of the building starting from the South Porch.

East and West Porch Bars
The Porches to the East and West of the Hall have now been glazed to form internal foyers, providing additional bars for the use and enjoyment of the Stalls audience.

Café Consort
Between February and the opening of the Proms, the old Prince Consort Restaurant is being enlarged and completely remodelled. The re-christened Café Consort will open two hours before each performance and provide some 200 covers with a wide range of food and refreshment. The striking design includes visual references to the conservatory that occupied the site to the South of the Hall in the 19th century.

The Organ
Audiences will be all too aware that, for the second year running, the Proms will be deprived of the Royal Albert Hall organ. The aim of the restoration, due for completion in December, has been to make as few changes as possible to the character and special qualities of the instrument. Overall, there will be some refinement in the sound and a significant increase in power when it is restored to its full glory in 2004.

The Auditorium
Since last summer, decoration has been completed of the plaster cove that runs around the base of the dome. New lighting schemes, designed to enhance appreciation of the architectural features of the auditorium, have also been introduced.

Funding the Development
The total cost of the programme will be just over £70m. £40m was provided by grants from the Arts Council of England and Heritage Lottery Funds. The Hall, which receives no funding from either central or local government, is close to raising the remaining £30m. Many audience members have generously contributed to a recent appeal but there is still a little under £2m left to raise. Your support would be most gratefully received; those interested should contact Sarah Dixon, Head of Development Fundraising, on 020 7589 3203 or email fund@royalalberthall.com

Beyond the Development
With the completion of the development, the Hall plans to channel some of the money it generates each year towards a programme of education work and to facilitate new strands of programming, fulfilling Prince Albert's original vision that the Royal Albert Hall should be dedicated to the promotion of the Arts and Sciences.

How to Prom

What is Promming?

The popular tradition of Promming is central to the unique and informal atmosphere of the BBC Proms.

Up to 1,400 standing places are available at each Proms concert. The traditionally low prices allow you to enjoy world-class concerts for just £4.00 each (or even less with a Season Ticket or Weekend Promming Pass).

There are two standing areas: the Arena, which is located directly in front of the stage, and the Gallery, running round the top of the Hall. All spaces are unreserved.

Day Prommers

Over 500 Arena and Gallery tickets (priced £4.00) go on sale on the day 30 minutes before doors open (one hour before on days when there are Pre-Prom talks). These tickets cannot be booked in advance, so even if all seats have been sold, you always have a good chance of getting in (though early queuing is obviously advisable for the more popular concerts). You must buy your ticket in person.

Day tickets are available (for cash only) at Door 11 (Arena) and Door 10 (Gallery), not at the Box Office. If in doubt about where to go, Royal Albert Hall stewards will point you in the right direction.

Season Tickets

Frequent Prommers can save money by purchasing Arena or Gallery Season Tickets covering either the whole Proms season or only the first or second half (ie Proms 1–36 or Proms 37–72).

Season Ticket-holders benefit from:
• guaranteed entrance (until 10 minutes before each concert)
• great savings – prices can work out at less than £2.00 per concert
• guaranteed entrance to the Last Night for Whole Season Ticket-holders and special access to a reserved allocation of Last Night tickets for Half Season Ticket-holders. See *opposite page.*

Please note that Season Ticket-holders arriving at the Royal Albert Hall later than 10 minutes before a concert are not guaranteed entry and may be asked, in certain circumstances, to join the day queue.

For further details and prices of Season Tickets, see page 121.

Weekend Promming Pass

WP The Weekend Promming Pass guarantees access to Proms at weekends and savings against Day Promming. *For full details, see page 113*

Where to Queue

● Arena Day Queue
Enter by Door 11

● Gallery Day Queue
Enter by Door 10

● Arena Season Queue
Enter by Door 2

● Gallery Season Queue
Enter by Door 3

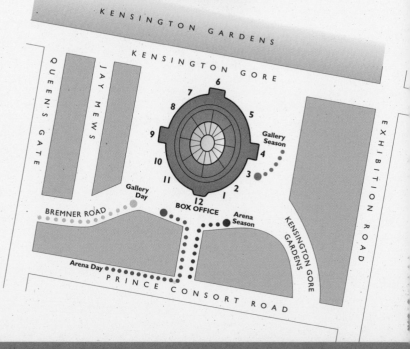

The Last Night

Owing to the huge demand for Last Night tickets, special booking arrangements apply. Your best chance of purchasing tickets for the Last Night of the Proms is through the Priority Booking syst...

Priority Booking for the Last Night

The Six Concert Rule

In order to apply for any tickets for the Last Night during the Priority Booking period (ie. before General Booking opens on Monday 16 June), you must book for at least six other concerts in the 2003 season.

Book one ticket in the same seating area for at least six other concerts in the 2003 season and you can apply at the same time for a single ticket in the same seating area for the Last Night. For example, book a ticket in the Choir for six concerts, and you can apply for one ticket in the Choir for the Last Night.

Book two or more tickets in the same seating area for at least six other concerts in the 2003 season and you can apply at the same time for a maximum of two tickets in the same seating area for the Last Night (ie. whether you book two or 22 Stalls tickets for six concerts, you can still apply for only two Stalls tickets for the Last Night).

Note that, if you book tickets for at least six other concerts but in different seating areas, you will be allocated Last Night seats in the area of the majority of your bookings (unless you specify that lower-priced tickets are desired).

We regret that, if the Last Night is sold out by the time your application is processed, no refunds for other tickets purchased will be payable.

General Booking for the Last Night

Once General Booking opens (on Monday 16 June), the 'Six Concert Rule' no longer applies. Note, however, that Last Night tickets have usually sold out by this stage.

Please note that, for all Last Night bookings, only one application (for a maximum of two tickets) can be made per household.

Promming at th...

Day Prommers an...
Promming Pass ho...

attended six or more (in either the Arena o... buy one ticket each fo... (priced £4.00) on pre... used tickets at the Bo... time after Wednesday... *to availability).*

Season Ticket-hold...

Season Tickets include... Last Night. A limited a... Night places is also re... Season Ticket-holders... Half Season Tickets ca... each (priced £4.00) at... from Wednesday 23 J... *availability).* Holders o...

Last Night Ballot Form

Title .... Initial ....

Surname ....

Address ....

....

....

Postcode ....

Country ....

Daytime tel. ....

Please tick the appropriate boxes

☐ I wish to apply for one ticket (£73.00)

☐ I wish to apply for two tickets (£146.00)

☐ I enclose a cheque made payable to 'Royal Albert Hall' and an SAE. (Cheques will be returned to unsuccessful applicants within two weeks of the ballot.)

☐ Please debit my Access/Visa/Amex/Mastercard/Switch*

Expiry Date ☐☐☐☐   Issue No.* ☐☐

Signature ....

Choose your seating area

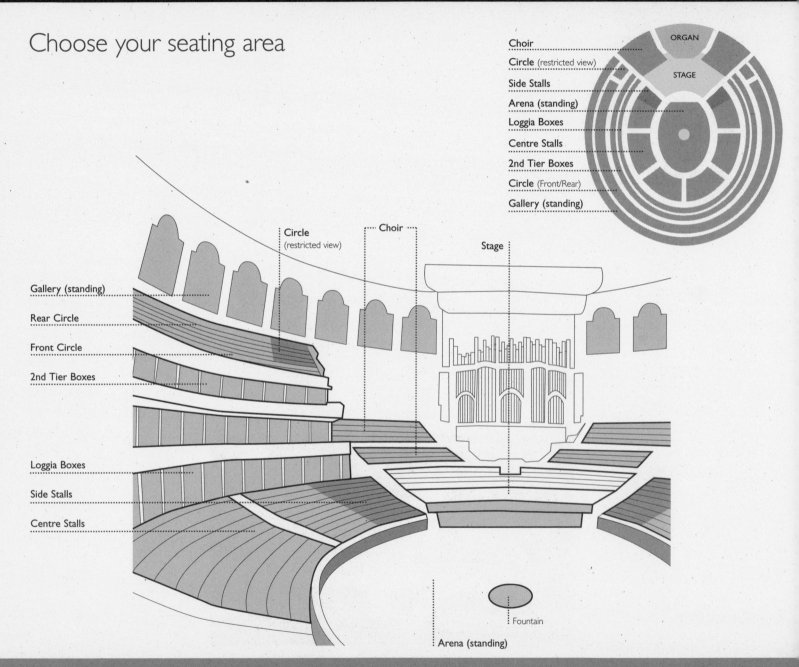

Choir
Circle (restricted view)
Side Stalls
Arena (standing)
Loggia Boxes
Centre Stalls
2nd Tier Boxes
Circle (Front/Rear)
Gallery (standing)

ORGAN
STAGE

Circle
(restricted view)

Choir

Stage

Gallery (standing)

Rear Circle

Front Circle

2nd Tier Boxes

Loggia Boxes

Side Stalls

Centre Stalls

Fountain

Arena (standing)

Price Bands for Proms in the Royal Albert Hall

Seats

Each concert falls into one of seven different price bands, colour coded for easy reference

	A	B	C	D	E	F	G
Centre Stalls	£23.00	£30.00	£38.00	£12.50	£15.00	£73.00	
Side Stalls	£21.50	£27.00	£35.00	£12.50	£15.00	£70.00	
Loggia Boxes (8 seats)	£25.00	£32.50	£40.00	£12.50	£15.00	£75.00	
2nd Tier Boxes (5 seats)	£17.50	£22.50	£32.00	£12.50	£15.00	£70.00	ALL SEATS £10.00 (UNDER-16s £5.00)
Choir	£15.00	£18.00	£24.00	£9.00	£12.50	£52.50	
Front Circle	£13.00	£16.00	£20.00	£9.00	£12.50	£52.50	
Rear Circle	£10.00	£11.00	£14.50	£9.00	£12.50	£40.00	
Circle (restricted view)	£6.00	£7.00	£10.00			£20.00	

Promming

Standing places are available in the Arena and Gallery on the day for £4.00 (see page 118)

Season Tickets	**Dates**	**Arena**	**Gallery**
Whole Season (Proms 1–73)	18 July – 13 September	**£160.00**	**£135.00**
Half Season tickets			
First Half (Proms 1–36)	18 July – 14 August	**£90.00**	**£75.00**
Second Half (Proms 37–72)	15 August – 12 September	**£90.00**	**£75.00**

BBC Proms in the Park, London, Saturday 13 September

All tickets £18.00   (for further details of this and other Proms in the Park venues, see page 109)

CBBC Prom in the Park, London, Sunday 14 September

Adults £12.00   **Children (3–16 yrs) £7.50**   **Under-3s free**

Please note that booking fees apply to all postal, fax, telephone and online bookings (for details, see Booking Form)

Ticket conditions

Tickets cannot be exchanged for other performances nor refunded except in the event of a cancelled performance.

Express booking
All forms including a request for an A band concert qualify as an express booking. To increase your chances of getting the tickets you request for the popular concerts in price bands B and C also book for an A band concert. If you are only booking for the *Blue Peter* Prom (price band G), your booking will also qualify for express booking. Tick the box at the end of the Booking Form if your application qualifies.

Disabled concert-goers
See page 116 for details of special discounts, access and facilities.

Privately owned seats
A high proportion of boxes, as well as 650 Stalls seats, are privately owned. Unless returned by owners, these seats are not available for sale.

Season tickets
Season tickets can be booked by post, fax or online from 19 May and by phone or in person at the Box Office from 16 June. For postal and fax bookings, complete the special section of the Booking Form (*facing page 122*). Two passport-sized photographs must be provided before tickets can be issued.

Proms Chamber Music
All seats £6.00, bookable in advance using the Booking Form (*facing page 122*) or via the Proms website.

Free events
Tickets for Proms Composer Portraits and the Proms Lecture are free and can be collected at the Proms Information Desk at the V&A (Exhibition Road entrance) from an hour beforehand. Pre-Prom Talks are free to ticket-holders for that evening's concert.

How to fill in the Priority Booking Form

- **Choose the concerts** you want to go to and where you want to sit.

- **Enter the number of tickets** you require for each concert under your chosen seating area.

- **Add up the value of tickets** requested and enter the amount in the 'Sub-total' column.

- **For the Proms Odyssey offer** (see page 112) and **Greek Myths Study Day** (see pages 134) complete the special sections of the Priority Booking Form.

- **For any other Special Offers** (see pages 112–113), tick the 'discount claimed' column and enter the value of the discount in the

'Discount' column. Subtract the value of the discount from the sub-total and enter the 'Total' at the end of the row.

- **For Under-16 discounts** (see page 113) enter the number of adults within the white area, the number of under-16s within the blue area.

- **If the tickets you want are not available**, lower-priced tickets for the same concert will be sent. Please tick the box at the end of the Booking Form if this is not acceptable.

Booking Queries

If you have any queries about how to fill in the Booking Form, call the Box Office on 020 7589 8212 (open 9.00am–9.00pm daily).

Fax Booking

If booking by fax, clearly state your name on all three pages. Please note that fax booking lines are open 24 hours a day. Please do not duplicate your booking by post or online.

Online Booking

For details of how to book online, visit the BBC Proms website at www.bbc.co.uk/proms

PRIORITY BOOKING FORM PART 1

First Name *ANNE*

Surname *D'ANTINO*

Full name of sender (fax bookings only)

Seating Area: please indicate number of tickets required

Prom	Date	Time	Price Code	Special Offers See pages 112–113	Centre Stalls	Side Stalls	Loggia Boxes (8 seats)	2nd Tier Boxes (5 seats)	Choir	Front Circle	Rear Circle	Circle (restricted view)	Wheelchair space See page 116	Sub-total (£)	Please tick if discount claimed	Discount (£)	Car Parking See page 115	Total (£)	Office Use
1	Friday 18 July	7.30	B		Number of adults				Number of under-16s					86:00	✓	21:50		64:50 26:00	
2	Saturday 19 July	7.00	A	16	2	2			2					26:00					
3	Sunday 20 July	7.00	A																
4	Monday 21 July	10.00	D															69:00	
5	Monday 21 July	7.30	A	16										69:00					
6	Tuesday 22 July	7.00	A		3									45:00	✓	12:00		33:00	
7	Wednesday 23 July	10.00	E		3														
8	Wednesday 23 July	7.30	A																
9	Thursday 24 July	7.30	A													✓	30:50	
10	Friday 25 July	11.00	G	16										23:00					
11	Saturday 26 July	7.30	A		1													32:00	
12	Saturday 26 July	7.30	A						2					32:00					
13	Sunday 27 July	7.30	B																
14	Monday 28 July	7.00	B																
15	Tuesday 29 July	10.00	D																
69	Wednesday 10 September	7.00	A																
70	Wednesday 10 September	10.00	E															118:80	
71	Thursday 11 September	7.30	C					12						132:00	✓	13:20			
72	Friday 12 September	7.30	B																
73	Saturday 13 September	7.45	F												Sub-total		373:80			

PRIORITY BOOKING FORM PART 1

Full name of sender (fax bookings only)

Surname _____ First Name _____

Seating Area: please indicate number of tickets required

Prom	Date	Time	Price Code	Special Offers See pages 112–113	Centre Stalls	Side Stalls	Loggia Boxes (8 seats)	2nd Tier Boxes (5 seats)	Choir	Front Circle	Rear Circle	Circle (restricted view)	Wheelchair space See page 116	Sub-total (£)	Please tick if discount claimed	Discount (£)	Car Parking See page 115	Total (£)	Office Use
1	Friday 18 July	7.30	B	G															
2	Saturday 19 July	7.00	A	(16)															
3	Sunday 20 July	7.00	A																
4	Monday 21 July	7.00	A										X						
5	Monday 21 July	10.00	D																
6	Tuesday 22 July	7.30	A										X						
7	Wednesday 23 July	7.00	A																
8	Wednesday 23 July	10.00	E																
9	Thursday 24 July	7.30	A																
10	Friday 25 July	7.30	A															X	
11	Saturday 26 July	11.00	G																
12	Saturday 26 July	7.30	A																
13	Sunday 27 July	7.30	A																
14	Monday 28 July	7.30	B										X						
15	Tuesday 29 July	7.00	B																
16	Tuesday 29 July	10.00	D																
17	Wednesday 30 July	7.30	A										X						
18	Thursday 31 July	7.00	A																
19	Friday 1 August	7.30	A																
20	Saturday 2 August	6.30	A																
21	Saturday 2 August	10.00	E																
22	Sunday 3 August	7.30	B										X						
23	Monday 4 August	7.00	C																
24	Tuesday 5 August	7.30	A																
25	...day 6 August	7.30	A																
26		7.30	A																

Number of adults **Number of under-16s**

BBC Proms, Box Office,
Royal Albert Hall, London SW7 2AP

Fax number:
020 7581 9311

If you fax this booking form, please do not duplicate ...

your order by post or online

PRIORITY BOOKING FORM PART 2

Full name of sender (fax bookings only)

Surname   First Name

Seating Area: please indicate number of tickets required

Prom	Date	Time	Price Code	Special Offers See pages 112–113	Centre Stalls	Side Stalls	Loggia Boxes (8 seats)	2nd Tier Boxes (5 seats)	Choir	Front Circle	Rear Circle	Circle (restricted view)	Wheelchair space See page 116	Sub-total (£)	Please tick if discount claimed	Discount (£)	Sub-total (£)	Car Parking See page 115	Total (£)	Office Use
65	Sunday 7 September	8.00	A																	
66	Monday 8 September	7.00	A																	
67	Monday 8 September	10.00	D																	
68	Tuesday 9 September	7.30	C									X								
69	Wednesday 10 September	7.00	A																	
70	Wednesday 10 September	10.00	E									X								
71	Thursday 11 September	7.30	C																	
72	Friday 12 September	7.30	B																	
73	Saturday 13 September	7.45	F																	

Total carried over

Sub-total

Proms Odyssey ◉

See page 112

You must book the same number of tickets in the same seating area for each concert. Prom 3 tickets purchased as part of the Greek Myths Study Day (*see below*) cannot be counted towards the Proms Odyssey offer.

Prom	Date	Time	Price Code	Centre Stalls	Side Stalls	Front Circle	Rear Circle	Car Parking See page 115	Wheelchair space See page 116	Total (£)
3	Sunday 20 July	7.00	A							
8	Wednesday 23 July	10.00	E							
15	Tuesday 29 July	7.00	B							

BBC Proms, Box Office, Royal Albert Hall, London SW7 2AP

Fax number:

020 7581 9311

If you fax this booking form, please do not duplicate your order by post or online

TEAR ALONG THE PERFORATED LINE

PRIORITY BOOKING FORM PART 3

Full name of sender (fax bookings only) Surname First Name

Proms Chamber Music, Mondays at 1.00pm **See pages 110–111**

All tickets £6.00		**Number of tickets**	**Total (£)**			**Number of tickets**	**Total (£)**
PCM 1	Monday 21 July		:	**PCM 5**	Monday 18 August		:
PCM 2	Monday 28 July		:	**PCM 6**	Monday 25 August		:
PCM 3	Monday 4 August		:	**PCM 7**	Monday 1 September		:
PCM 4	Monday 11 August		:	**PCM 8**	Monday 8 September		:
		Total to carry over	:			**Sub-total**	:

BBC Proms in the Park, London, Saturday 13 September

For details of this and other Proms in the Park venues, see page 109

	Number of tickets			**Total (£)**
All tickets £18.00 (under-3s free)			**Sub-total**	:

CBBC Prom in the Park, London, Sunday 14 September

	Number of tickets			**Total (£)**
Adult tickets: £12.00				:
Child tickets (3–16 yrs): £7.50 (under-3s free)				:
			Sub-total	:

Part 3 Total £ :

BBC Proms, Box Office,

Royal Albert Hall, London SW7 2AP

Fax number:

020 7581 9311

If you fax this booking form, please do not duplicate your order by post or online

The Nation's Favourites

For the first time, you can take part in choosing a Proms programme. Join the BBC Proms/*Radio Times* readers' poll to vote for the arias you would like to hear sung in 'The Nation's Favourite Prom' on Saturday 19 July

Choose from the following three shortlists the arias and duets that you would like Rosemary Joshua and John Mark Ainsley to sing:

A. SOPRANO SOLOS

1 **Bernstein** 'I feel pretty' (West Side Story)
2 **Gounod** 'Je veux vivre' (Romeo & Juliet)
3 **Mozart** 'Voi che sapete' (The Marriage of Figaro)
4 **Puccini** 'O mio babbino caro' (Gianni Schicchi)
5 **Rossini** 'Una voce poco fa' (The Barber of Seville)
6 **Verdi** 'Volta la terrea' (A Masked Ball)

B. TENOR SOLOS

1 **Donizetti** 'Una furtiva lagrima' (The Elixir of Love)
2 **Handel** 'Where'er you walk' (Semele)
3 **Mozart** 'Dies Bildnis ist bezaubernd schön' (The Magic Flute)
4 **Novello** 'We'll gather lilacs'

C. SOPRANO/TENOR DUETS

1 **Beethoven** 'Jetzt, Schätzchen, jetzt sind wir allein' (Fidelio)
2 **Bernstein** 'One hand, one heart' (West Side Story)
3 **Donizetti** 'Tornami a dir che m'ami' (Don Pasquale)
4 **Lehár** 'Lippen schweigen' (The Merry Widow)

Vote for one choice in each of the three categories A, B and C, listing your selection by number, eg. A5, B3, C2

• **Vote by telephone on 08700 100 300**
(calls charged at national rate)

• **Listen to sound clips and vote online at www.bbc.co.uk/proms**

Votes must be submitted by Friday 13 June

And remember, even if you can't attend 'The Nation's Favourite Prom' yourself, you can hear it live on BBC Radio 3 or watch it on BBC1 on Sunday 20 July.

Proms Question Time
Money Well Spent?

Friday 25 July, c9.45–10.30pm
(following Prom 10)
West Arena Foyer

Admission free to ticket-holders for Prom 10

Christopher Cook chairs a debate on the relevance of contemporary music to today's concert-goers. A chance for you, the Proms audience, to react to recent premieres and to cross-examine a panel that will include Marin Alsop, Joe Duddell and Colin Currie – the conductor, composer and dedicatee of the night's new BBC commission (see *New Music, pages 66–75*). You can also take part in the debate online via the BBC Proms website at www.bbc.co.uk/proms.

The Lanson Foyer will be open for refreshments during the debate.

For Proms Composer Portraits and Pre-Prom Talks, see page 136

RIGHT
John Mark Ainsley and Rosemary Joshua as Jupiter and his latest conquest in English National Opera's 1999 staging of Handel's mythological oratorio *Semele*

FAR RIGHT
Christopher Cook, Marin Alsop, Joe Duddell and Colin Currie

BBC Proms in the Park

This year, for the very first time, audiences in all four nations of the UK get to share in the unique festive atmosphere of the Last Night of the Proms, as BBC Proms in the Park reaches out to London, Belfast, Swansea – and now Glasgow too

London, Belfast, Swansea, Glasgow

Saturday 13 September

See page 109 for booking details

ABOVE
Your host in Hyde Park:
Terry Wogan

Now in its eighth year, BBC Proms in the Park continues to offer a colourful conclusion to the summer Proms season, attracting capacity crowds to share in the unique communal spirit of the Last Night of the Proms, whether in London's Hyde Park (where it all began in 1996) or in an ever-increasing variety of other venues across the UK.

In 1999, Wales hosted its first ever Prom in the Park, and this year the BBC National Orchestra of Wales is back in Singleton Park, Swansea, once again (under conductor Peter Stark) for a

programme that features renowned tenor Robert Tear, alongside Catrin Finch, Harpist to the Prince of Wales, and Swansea-born singer/songwriter Steve Balsamo.

Last year, Northern Ireland joined the Last Night party for the very first time, and the Ulster Orchestra will be back in the grounds of Belfast's City Hall again this year to play its part in the festive celebrations.

This year, it is Scotland's turn to enter into the Last Night spirit. With the BBC Scottish Symphony Orchestra hosting the first ever Proms in the Park event north of the border – in front of Glasgow's stunning new Science Centre on the side of the Clyde at Pacific Quay –

audiences from all four nations in the United Kingdom can at last take part in the traditional music and merriment of the Last Night of the Proms.

As ever, the evening's entertainment in Hyde Park, London, is hosted by the inimitable and irrepressible Mr Terry Wogan. Robin Stapleton conducts the BBC Concert Orchestra, chic French pianist Jean-Yves Thibaudet tickles the ivories, and West End musical star Ruthie Henshall and top Welsh bass-baritone Bryn Terfel (who famously sang 'Rule, Britannia!' – in Welsh and full rugby kit – inside the Royal Albert Hall in 1994) share

the stage in a selection of well-loved songs and arias. And, as the afternoon's prelude to the evening's broadcast event, Ken Bruce presents the Grimethorpe Colliery (UK Coal) Band – as seen and heard in the film *Brassed Off* – and 10-piece Motown tribute band, Soulfish.

As always, all four concerts culminate in live big-screen link-ups with the proceedings inside the Royal Albert Hall, where Leonard Slatkin conducts the BBC Symphony Orchestra for his third Last Night of the Proms.

Saturday 13 September
For further details and booking information, see page 109 or the Proms website www.bbc.co.uk/proms

Events sponsored by
RENAULT

ABOVE (FROM LEFT TO RIGHT)
The BBC Concert Orchestra and star guests Bryn Terfel, Ruthie Henshall and Jean-Yves Thibaudet, plus the Grimethorpe Colliery Band, will all be appearing in London's Hyde Park, while singers Steve Balsamo and Robert Tear will share the stage with royal harpist Catrin Finch (*below*) in Singleton Park, Swansea

RIGHT
Angellica Bell and Matt Baker

LEFT
City Hall, Belfast, and the new Science Centre, Glasgow: venues for this year's events in Northern Ireland and Scotland

CBBC Prom in the Park

Once again this year Hyde Park will continue to party even after the Last Night of the Proms is all over, as CBBC's Angellica Bell and Matt Baker host the fourth CBBC Prom in the Park.

So why not take the kids along on Sunday 14 September for a fun-filled family afternoon featuring the BBC Philharmonic (conductor Philip Ellis) with top acts from the charts and favourite stars from CBBC programmes.

CBBC Prom in the Park
Sunday 14 September
Hyde Park, London
Gates open 1.00pm
Entertainment on stage from 2.30pm

For further details and booking information, see page 109 or the Proms website www.bbc.co.uk/proms

The BBC Proms reach out …

… with a special pre-season event in Brixton for new audiences, our now-annual Young Composers Competition and Concert, and a John Adams-led education project for teenagers

**BBC Proms:
out & about**
Friday 27 June, 6.00pm
Brixton Academy
London SW9

*Call 08700 100 300
for ticketing details*

**BBC Proms/Guardian
Young Composers
Concert**
Friday 25 July, 2.00pm
Lecture Theatre
Victoria & Albert Museum

*Invitation concert: for details
see www.bbc.co.uk/proms*

Memory Spaces
**Sunday 27 July,
4.00pm–10.30pm**
Gulbenkian Upper Gallery
Royal College of Art

Admission free

ABOVE
Tributes to lost loved ones
left at 'Ground Zero'

The aim of the Proms has always been to draw new audiences to music-making of the highest quality. It has achieved this through a combination of top-rank artists, adventurous programming and the broadcasting of every concert. In a new century we need to try new methods of achieving these aims, and to continue to open up the Proms. So this year, for the first time, the Proms go 'out & about' to meet a new audience, and will present an innovative pre-season event at the Brixton Academy, South London, in June.

One of the world's most exciting composers, John Adams is famed for his ability to communicate contemporary concerns in an up-to-date musical language, not least in such works as the operas *Nixon in China* and *The Death of Klinghoffer* that he created in collaboration with this year's Proms lecturer, the director Peter Sellars (*see*

opposite). Adams is just beginning a new relationship with the BBC Symphony Orchestra and, in the run-up to this year's Proms season, they will together create this unique new event: inspiring, fun – educative but more than education – it will be a powerful, inclusive experience that will aim to draw a new audience to the best of modern music.

BBC Proms: out & about will showcase some of the most thrilling extracts from 20th-century music. It will introduce the orchestra to audiences who may never have heard one before. And it will demonstrate what the Proms have always proved – that, to open ears, the newest of new music is exciting and engaging. The first conductor of the Proms, Henry Wood, always on the search for novelties and always wishing to bring music to a wider audience, would surely applaud this latest BBC initiative.

ABOVE
The Statue of Liberty rises above a smoke-filled
New York skyline, 11 September 2001;
John Adams (*inset*)

Memory Spaces

On the Transmigration of Souls, John Adams's moving new work written in response to the events of 11 September 2001, receives its European premiere in Prom 13 (see 'New Music', pages 66–75). It also provides the focus for this year's Proms education project, *Memory Spaces*, in which teenagers will work with musicians and other artists to explore the use of artistic expression as a means of articulating reactions to world events. Adams himself will meet those involved in the project to explain how, in his new work, he tried to absorb and reflect the emotions of the aftermath of 9/11, as expressed in tributes to lost loved ones left at 'Ground Zero'.

The art pieces, poetry and music created during the project will be presented in a *Memory Spaces* installation at the Royal College of Art, which will be open to the public both before and after Prom 13.

Young Composers Concert

A new, and widely welcomed, innovation last year was the first BBC Proms/Guardian Young Composers Concert, featuring works submitted for our annual competition. The works, by composers aged from 12 to 18, were also broadcast on BBC Radio 3.

This year's Young Composers Competition has already been launched in *The Guardian*. James MacMillan, who wrote there about what made him want to become a composer, joins fellow composers Joe Duddell, Jocelyn Pook and Fraser Trainer on the judging panel for this year's awards. You can hear all last year's winners and find out about this year's competition and concert on the BBC Proms website: www.bbc.co.uk/proms

Associated Press

The BBC Proms Lecture 2003

This year's lecturer, the American theatre director Peter Sellars, tells Rik Breefe **why modern democracy depends on ancient myths**

'The Culture of Democracy'
Sunday 3 August, 5.30pm
Lecture Theatre, Victoria & Albert Museum (Exhibition Road entrance)

Recorded for broadcast on BBC Radio 3 on Sunday 10 August, 5.45pm

Admission to the BBC Proms Lecture is free, but availability is limited. Tickets can be collected from the Proms Information Desk at the V&A from an hour beforehand. Latecomers will not be admitted.

BELOW
A scene from Peter Sellars's recent staging of Euripides' 5th-century BC refugee drama, *The Children of Herakles*

Spiky hairdo aside, Peter Sellars is best known for his engagement with modern America, whether in his time-shift stagings of classic operas – setting Mozart's *Figaro* in Trump Tower, for example, and Handel's *Orlando* in the Kennedy Space Center – or in the CNN-style 'living history' operas he has created with the composer John Adams, starting with their 1987 diplomatic comedy, *Nixon in China*, about the disgraced President's historic visit to Peking.

But Sellars has always been equally engaged with ancient Greece, returning to its drama regularly throughout his career – 'once every five years,' he recently joked, 'whenever things get dangerous!' Thus in 1987 he set Sophocles' *Ajax* in the Pentagon 'in order to explore the ravaging effects of the Vietnam War', while in 1993, in the wake of the first Gulf War, he staged Aeschylus' *The Persians* – the earliest extant play in Western literature, and an extraordinary attempt to see the effects of a recent Greek victory from the losers' point of view – at the court of Saddam Hussein.

As Sellars says of the Greeks, 'We inherited two main things from those guys. One is democracy, the other is culture – and, forgive me,' he adds with a laugh, 'but I think they're related!'

How? Because, in his view, theatre itself was invented – in Athens, the world's first democracy – 'to prepare citizens for jury duty, so that they could learn to judge what was just or unjust in complicated cases'. Thanks to the rich store of mythological tales on which the Athenian dramatists drew, '20,000 citizens would be sitting there in an amphitheatre on the side of town watching detailed discussions of such complex issues as rape, incest and murder, or how you treated the prisoners in the last war – everything that it's impossible to speak about in polite conversation.'

The fact that, after a more than five-year lull, Sellars is now deep into another Greek phase suggests that he at least thinks things are getting 'dangerous' again. Last autumn he staged Euripides' *The Children of Herakles* as a devastatingly stripped-down exploration of the plight of refugees. In January, his version of Antonin Artaud's *For an End to the Judgement of God*, staged as a Pentagon Press Conference addressed by a mad general (and intercut with footage from the Afghan War), was given at Tate Modern under one of the three 'gigantic screaming mouths' of *Marsyas*, Anish Kapoor's massive installation named after the mythical satyr who was flayed alive for daring to challenge Apollo's musical

prowess. And Kapoor is also designing the new staging of Mozart's mythological opera *Idomeneo* that Sellars is directing at Glyndebourne this summer.

As Sellars says, speaking by phone from California on the day of the Bush–Blair summit in the Azores, the story of the Cretan commander-in-chief who gets caught in a storm while sailing home from the sack of Troy, and saves his life by vowing to sacrifice the first living creature he sees – only to find his own son waiting for him on shore – is 'right there, it could not be more precise. It's one of the key questions, whenever we engage in these foreign wars: who must be sacrificed? That's why these myths remain so central, however much our context shifts.'

RIGHT
Peter Sellars

BELOW
Cradle of democracy: the Theatre of Dionysus, beside the Acropolis in Athens

Myths at the museum

Special guided tours, gallery talks and a Greek Myths Study Day – all at the British Museum

The British Museum
Great Russell Street,
London WC1

ABOVE RIGHT
The Great Court
at the British Museum

ABOVE LEFT
Oedipus and the Sphinx:
5th-century BC Greek vase, on
show at the British Museum

BELOW
The face of war: Corinthian
bronze helmet (c500 BC), on
show at the British Museum

The British Museum is one of the best places to explore myths from many world cultures, including those of ancient Greece. Greek myths feature both in dedicated displays that tell famous stories through ancient images, and on many other objects throughout the Greek and Roman galleries.

The Greek galleries (Main Floor, Rooms 11–23) cover a wide range of myths, from early legends, such as the Minotaur in Minoan Crete, to Classical and later images of gods, goddesses and heroes, including such well-known figures as Achilles, Medea, Athene and Zeus. In the dedicated 'Greek and Roman Life' displays (Upper Floor, Room 69) the visitor can follow the dramatic events of the Trojan War unfolding in ancient Greek and Roman images, witness the deeds of Herakles and Theseus, learn about the Greek and Roman gods, and see such famous scenes as Odysseus' encounter with the Sirens depicted on ancient Greek pottery. Other galleries include representations of various myths in sculpture (Lower Floor, Rooms 83–84) and further explore the development of myths in South Italian, Etruscan, Roman and Cypriot art (Upper Floor, Rooms 70–73).

GREEK MYTHS STUDY DAY
Saturday 19 July, 10.00am–4.30pm
BP Theatre, Clore Education Centre,
The British Museum (Lower Floor)

In preparation for the following day's performance of Michael Tippett's Trojan War opera *King Priam*, leading experts from the British Museum and elsewhere examine the historical background to the Greek myths and their representation in art, opera, theatre and film.

Schedule for the day:
Introduction John Reeve (Head of Education, British Museum)
Session 1: The Trojan War in the British Museum George Hart and Lesley Fitton (British Museum)
Session 2: Greek Myths in the Opera House Patrick Bade (Christie's Education)
Session 3: Greek Myths in the Theatre Russell Shone (University College London) with Chloë Productions
Session 4: Greek Myths on Film Margaret O'Brien (British Museum)

OTHER PROMS-RELATED EVENTS

Daily Tours
Daily Tours of the Greek Galleries are led by specially trained volunteer guides.

Gallery Talks
A special series of gallery talks on the Greek myths will take place during the Proms season. 11.15am Monday–Friday, plus some Saturdays.

www.thebritishmuseum.ac.uk
Visit the British Museum website for special features on Greek myths as well as full details of all guided tours, gallery talks and special Proms-related events.

Alternatively, for a special events leaflet, telephone 020 7323 8511/8854, e-mail education@thebritishmuseum.ac.uk or write to: BBC Proms & British Museum Education (Greek Myths), The British Museum, London WC1B 3DG

Greek Myths Study Day
Tickets for Study Day only: £28 (BM Friends £25; concessions £18)
Bookable via the British Museum Box Office
By post: The Box Office, The British Museum, London WC1B 3DG (cheques payable to The British Museum Great Court Ltd)
By telephone (from 19 May): 020 7323 8181
Online at www.thebritishmuseum.ac.uk

Special Proms Package
Includes admission to the Greek Myths Study Day plus a Stalls ticket to the following day's performance of Tippett's *King Priam* (Prom 3) for only £35 (a saving of £16)
Bookable by post, using the Priority Booking Form (facing page 122), or by telephone (from 16 June) on 020 7589 8212
Places are subject to availability.

Proms at the pictures

A summer season of free lunchtime talks at the National Gallery

The National Gallery
Trafalgar Square,
London WC2

All talks begin at 1.00pm
(and last 40–50 minutes)

Admission is free;
no booking is required

ABOVE
Oedipus and the Sphinx (c1826)
by Jean-Auguste-Dominique
Ingres (1780–1867), on show
at the National Gallery

ABOVE RIGHT
Apollo and Daphne (c1475)
by Antonio del Pollaiuolo
(c1432–98), on show at the
National Gallery

BOTTOM RIGHT
The National Gallery

To complement this year's Proms theme, the National Gallery is organising a summer season of free lunchtime talks about myth-related art in its collection.

Just as composers have explored the rich resources of Greek mythology for creative inspiration, so artists too have used these vivid characters and their lives as the starting-point for pictures. Oedipus, Medea, Ariadne, Odysseus – the cast-list is packed with famous names whose stories offer compelling dramas of love, betrayal, loss and discovery.

The National Gallery has some of the world's finest examples of mythological painting, and has put together an exciting programme of talks so that art-loving Proms-goers can enjoy looking as well as listening.

In addition to slide-lectures in the air-conditioned Sainsbury Wing Theatre, there will be guided tours and gallery talks held in front of the paintings themselves (stools will be provided).

These will range from general introductions to in-depth examinations of particular Greek myths and, wherever possible, will relate directly to specific Proms concerts. So, on some days, you could be looking at an artistic representation of a particular myth in the National Gallery at lunchtime, then listening to a musical interpretation of the same narrative at a Prom that night.

The season is divided into three parts:

Painting Greek Myths
Friday 18 July – Saturday 2 August
Slide-lectures and gallery talks on how and why artists have depicted particular characters and their stories.

Myths on the Move
Tuesday 5 August –
Saturday 30 August
'Promenade' gallery tours looking at a picture of a Greek myth and other highlight paintings in the collection.

Myth-making
Tuesday 2 September –
Saturday 13 September
Slide-lectures and gallery talks setting Greek myths into a broader exploration of narrative art.

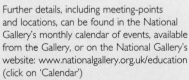

Further details, including meeting-points and locations, can be found in the National Gallery's monthly calendar of events, available from the Gallery, or on the National Gallery's website: www.nationalgallery.org.uk/education (click on 'Calendar')
The National Gallery offers free lunchtime lectures and gallery talks every day throughout the year, along with many other events, family activities, courses and workshops.

For information, call 020 7747 2885
or visit www.nationalgallery.org.uk

Proms Composer Portraits

**Lecture Theatre,
Victoria & Albert
Museum**

(Exhibition Road entrance)

*Recorded for broadcast on
BBC Radio 3 later the same
day, immediately following
the main-evening Prom*

*Admission is free, but availability
is limited. Tickets can be
collected from the Proms
Information Desk at the V&A
from an hour beforehand.
Latecomers will not be
admitted until a suitable
break in the performance.*

This year, four Proms Composer Portraits feature music for chamber ensemble by five contrasting composers, four of whom have works being performed in that night's Prom and two of whom are being introduced to Proms audiences for the first time: the young German, Matthias Pintscher, and the dynamic Chinese-American, Chen Yi, who also sings in one of her own pieces. In each of these early-evening events, the composer, in conversation with BBC Radio 3's Andrew McGregor, will discuss the work being heard in the main-evening Prom,

while also presenting a different aspect of their creativity through smaller-scale pieces, to be performed by young musicians from leading music colleges and conservatoires around the UK. The series opens with the well-known Scottish composer Judith Weir, and the final Portrait offers an opportunity to hear composer and broadcaster Michael Berkeley talk not only about his own music but also about that of his father, centenary composer Lennox Berkeley (whose *Magnificat* is heard the following night).

Judith Weir
Thursday 7 August, 6.00pm
(before Prom 26)
Music for 247 strings; Sketches
from a Bagpiper's Album;
Distance and Enchantment

Chen Yi
Tuesday 19 August, 6.00pm
(before Prom 41)
Duo Ye; As in a Dream; Qi

Matthias Pintscher
Tuesday 2 September,
5.30pm (before Prom 57)
Figura V/Assonanza; Lieder
und Schneebilder

**Michael and
Lennox Berkeley**
Thursday 4 September,
6.00pm (before Prom 60)
Michael Berkeley: Catch Me If
You Can, for wind quintet
Lennox Berkeley: Sonatina for guitar

Pre-Prom Talks

RAH • Royal Albert Hall
(Auditorium: Door 6)
**RCM • Royal College
of Music**

*Admission is free to ticket-
holders for the following Prom.*

Friday 18 July, 6.00pm RCM
Dennis Marks on Prokofiev's *Ivan the Terrible*

Sunday 20 July, 5.30pm RAH
Meirion Bowen on Tippett's *King Priam*

Tuesday 22 July, 6.00pm RAH
Nicholas Kenyon and Andrew Manze

Thursday 24 July, 6.00pm RAH
James MacMillan on his Symphony No. 3

Friday 25 July, 6.00pm RAH
Joe Duddell and Colin Currie talk to Verity Sharp

Sunday 27 July, 6.00pm RCM
John Adams in conversation

Monday 28 July, 6.00pm RCM
Sir John Eliot Gardiner on Berlioz

Tuesday 29 July, 5.30pm RCM
Rodney Milnes on Richard Strauss's *Elektra*

Friday 1 August, 6.00pm RAH
Erkki-Sven Tüür talks to Andrew Kurowski

Monday 4 August, 5.30pm RAH
Patrick O'Connor on Johann Strauss's *Fledermaus*

Wednesday 6 August, 6.00pm RAH
Sally Beamish and Håkan Hardenberger
talk to Stephen Johnson

Friday 8 August, 5.30pm RCM
Richard Steinitz on Ligeti

Sunday 10 August, 6.00pm RAH
Stephen Walsh on Stravinsky's *Perséphone*
and Poulenc's *La voix humaine*

Monday 11 August, 5.30pm RCM
Marina Frolova-Walker on *Alexander Nevsky*

Thursday 14 August, 5.30pm RCM
Gillian Moore on Knussen and Carter

Friday 15 August, 6.00pm RAH
Calum MacDonald on Brahms's Requiem

Sunday 17 August, 5.30pm RAH
Piers Burton-Page on Berlioz's *Benvenuto Cellini*

Monday 18 August, 6.00pm RAH
Tuomas Kinberg, General Manager of the Lahti
Symphony Orchestra, talks to Mark Lowther

Wednesday 20 August, 6.00pm RAH
David Fanning on Prokofiev

Friday 22 August, 6.00pm RAH
Daniel Barenboim and Edward Said

Sunday 24 August, 5.30pm RAH
Paul McCreesh talks to Ruth Smith about *Saul*

Thursday 28 August, 6.00pm RAH
Sakari Oramo talks to Stephen Maddock

Saturday 30 August, 5.30pm RAH
Members of Pittsburgh Symphony Orchestra

Monday 1 September, 6.00pm RAH
Heiner Goebbels talks to John Tusa

Saturday 6 September, 5.00pm RAH
David Nice on Prokofiev's *War and Peace*

Sunday 7 September, 6.30pm RCM
Stephen Johnson on Stravinsky's *Oedipus rex*

Wednesday 10 September, 5.15pm RAH
Audience Forum: with Nicholas Kenyon
and David Elliott

Friday 12 September, 6.00pm RAH
Sir Harrison Birtwistle talks to Jonathan Cross

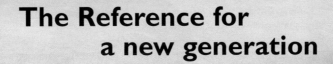

BBC PROMS collectables

designed by Brian Grimwood

Available from June 2003 in the BBC shops

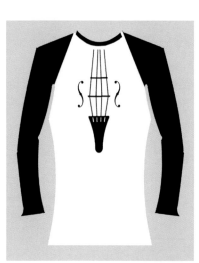

www.bbcshop.com

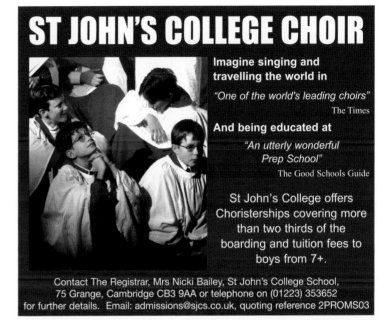

Still the best seat in the hall

Lynne Walker talks to Roger Wright and colleagues about Radio 3's plans to make the Proms the pinnacle of your listening experience

The audience for the Proms is getting bigger. Whether via radio, television or the internet, more people than could ever get to the concerts themselves are choosing either to switch on, flick on or click on. For Roger Wright, the Controller of BBC Radio 3, taking the Proms to where people want their entertainment to be, where they are most comfortable listening, is almost an obsession. 'There is this notion that listeners look up the *Radio Times*, then turn on their radio and tune in to that evening's concert. But we can't any longer assume regular, informed listening habits. That's all gone, and the traditional broadcasting media are now complemented by many other ways of listening.'

So every Prom is now not only broadcast on Radio 3 but streamed live via the website (www.bbc.co.uk/proms), while many are also made available as 'Audio on Demand' (allowing for 'time-shifted' listening). Thanks to the BBC's new 'free-to-air' TV services, all Radio 3 broadcasts can now also be accessed digitally via a 'set-top box' – something that has brought improved reception for many listeners. In addition, all the BBC4 digital TV relays, plus the BBC1 and BBC2 live broadcasts of the First and Last Nights, will be video-webcast on the Proms website. 'People can now control how, when and where they listen to the Proms,' says Wright. 'Our role at Radio 3 is to provide a gateway to the concerts, and to related content elsewhere on the network.'

With 10 of this season's concerts going out on BBC1 and BBC2, and 14 more on BBC4, might not all these methods of tuning in to the Proms deter people from actually going to the Royal Albert Hall? 'Quite the contrary,' replies Wright. 'As with a football match or any live event, while it's great being able to listen to it on the radio or watch it on TV, and while the profile of the event is undoubtedly raised by a live broadcast, of course there's still nothing like being there in person.'

But there's a lot to be gained too from a front-row position on the Radio 3 touchline. As Edward Blakeman, Radio 3's Executive Producer for the Proms, sees it, 'We're really creating a special event for listeners. Of course, Radio 3 is totally dependent on the concert in the Royal Albert Hall, with its own live edge and atmosphere. But when radio is at its most vivid, it is speaking absolutely directly and intimately to you or me, the listener, wherever we are.

'The colour and context the presenters bring to each performance, and the atmosphere we create on air, are as important as ensuring the best possible broadcast sound for the music itself. Exclusive "add-ons" for the listener – a few words of introduction from the soloist recorded at the rehearsal, a perceptive comment from

BOTTOM LEFT
'We go over now to the Royal Albert Hall for tonight's Prom': the view across the Arena from the Radio 3 commentary box

BELOW
A new generation of artists on Radio 3: Alice Coote, Jonathan Lemalu, Lawrence Power

ABOVE
Janine Jansen, Li-Wei, the
Karol Szymanowski Quartet

TOP RIGHT
The Galliard Ensemble

a conductor, or a short introduction to a rare work from an enthusiast – provide something that you can't get in the hall. In many ways, listening at home or in the car or at your computer gives you more, not less.'

'The great thing,' says Wright, 'is that every Prom is broadcast live. For eight weeks the Proms dominate Radio 3's summer schedule and are an integral part of the network's output.' It obviously helps that the Director of the Proms and the Controller of Radio 3 share the same ethos. 'Nick [Kenyon] and I are both passionate about the same things – new commissions, open and easy access, attracting as wide a listening public as possible to new cultural experiences. A high quality of music-making, an eclectic range of orchestras, ensembles and soloists, and exciting repertoire pretty much define the Proms and are at the heart of Radio 3 throughout the year. It's a tremendous resource and the more windows on these concerts that we at Radio 3 can open, arousing curiosity and interest, the better. And everything that happens in or around the Proms is closely related to what Radio 3 is providing all the time.'

One of those common interests is the nurturing of new, young performers waiting in the wings, particularly through Radio 3's 'New Generation Artists' scheme. The Proms audience has always given an especially warm welcome to newcomers and, as Adam Gatehouse, Executive Producer for the New Generation Artists, explains, 'From the beginning of the scheme in 1999 the

Proms have been one of the four main pillars – the jewel in the crown of the schedule of studio recordings, public concerts and engagements with BBC orchestras that we arrange for our New Generation Artists.'

Six new New Generation Artists are taken on each year – with each attachment lasting for two years. Of the current crop of 12, five soloists and two ensembles will be featured at this year's Proms, as well as three past members of the scheme. 'Getting a Prom is a terrific opportunity for any New Generation Artist,' says Gatehouse, 'whether it's a major evening concert on the stage of the Royal Albert Hall or a Proms Chamber Music recital at the V&A. It's obviously important to find the repertoire that suits both the performer's personality and musical range.'

So this season, playing to each artist's strengths, we have the Dutch violinist Janine Jansen starring in 'The Nation's Favourite Prom', the Chinese-Australian cellist Li-Wei showing his formidable RNCM-nurtured talent in Prokofiev's Cello Concerto, the Juilliard-trained British viola player Lawrence Power tackling Berlioz's *Harold in Italy*, and the Kathleen Ferrier Prize-winning New Zealand-born bass-baritone Jonathan Lemalu singing in Berlioz's *The Trojans* with Sir Colin Davis and the LSO. The Karol Szymanowski Quartet and the Galliard Ensemble wind quintet will both be performing in the Monday-lunchtime PCM series at the V&A, as will the

mezzo-soprano Alice Coote, for whom the composer Judith Weir has been commissioned to write a new song-cycle. Former New Generation Artists Paul Lewis, Christopher Maltman and James Rutherford are also appearing.

Gatehouse is justifiably proud of what Radio 3's New Generation Artists have already gone on to achieve. 'No other organisation in the world has a scheme like this – and an invitation to appear at the Proms really does represent the icing on the cake.'

Radio 3 New Generation Artists at the Proms 2003

Current members of the scheme	
Alice Coote	PROM 12
	& PCM 4
Galliard Ensemble	PCM 1
Janine Jansen	PROM 2
Jonathan Lemalu	PROMS 47 & 48
Li-Wei	PROM 34
Lawrence Power	PROM 29
Szymanowski Quartet	PCM 6
Former members of the scheme	
Paul Lewis	PROM 51
Christopher Maltman	PROM 39
James Rutherford	PROM 1

Press red for (inter)action

Thanks to the BBC's digital services, says Graeme Kay, **this year's Proms season will be even more interactive than ever**

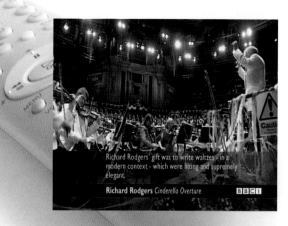

Richard Rodgers' gift was to write waltzes - in a modern context - which were lilting and supremely elegant.

Richard Rodgers Cinderella Overture

We've come a long way since TV audiences saw Siegfried gingerly uncovering the sleeping Brünnhilde, uttering the immortal line 'Das ist kein Mann!', and moments later the caption generator helpfully explaining 'That's not a man!' This was as far as in-vision prompting could go in the early 1980s, when the BBC broadcast the Bayreuth centenary production of Wagner's *Ring*.

By contrast, if you had access to digital TV, and you tuned in to last year's Last Night of the Proms, you'd have been treated to fully contextualised in-vision programme notes, presented in a stylish bar at the foot of the screen. A couple of miles from the Royal Albert Hall, at TV Centre in Shepherd's Bush, these notes were being cued from the score, in real time, at the BBC's state-of-the-art Interactive Production Suite. The feedback was immediate: the BBC was bombarded with e-mails saying, 'More, please!' And in 2003, more there definitely shall be.

The 2002 Proms marked the roll-out of many new interactive services; BBC4 had just been launched and broadcast all the first fortnight's Proms. A new style of presentation was put in place: conductor Charles Hazlewood anchored the broadcasts from a Grand Tier box that began to resemble an internet café, as composers, critics, performers and pundits joined him to discuss the concerts. Nikolaj Znaider climbed the stairs, still perspiring from his performance of Nielsen's Violin Concerto. One night, Rory Bremner dropped by for a chat, and stayed on afterwards to watch what went on. There wasn't much room: also shoehorned into the box were members of the Proms interactive team, setting up the live streaming of the concerts on the Proms website, and editing viewers' and listeners' e-mails for Charles to read out. As well as reactions to the music, there was an amusing thread of reaction to Charles's choice of shirts. Meanwhile, down in the Arena, Prommers' views were being canvassed, with roving reporter Clare-Louise Stuart popping back-stage to watch the musicians prepare – when the Russians come, that usually means serious games of chess.

These interactive elements offer just a foretaste of what viewers can expect when the analogue transmitters are eventually switched off and digital becomes the new standard. The driving-force behind the interactive proposition for the Proms is a desire to enrich users' experience in every possible way, and to share the excitement and 'liveness' of a supreme musical event with the largest number of people.

The palpable success of the 2002 experience has encouraged the BBC to expand its range of services in 2003. For viewers via Digital Satellite and Freeview, in-vision programme notes will be available for the first fortnight of Proms on BBC4, plus nine further Proms on BBC1 and BBC2. Contextualised notes and texts for the audience-participation items will be available again for Part 2 of the Last Night on BBC1, while Digital Satellite and Freeview viewers watching Part 1 of the Last Night on BBC2 will also be able to access the London 'Prom in the Park' event in Hyde Park by pressing the red button on their remote controls. Viewers with Digital Cable can access additional Proms information by pressing the 'Interactive' button on their remote controls. There's also a big expansion in the BBC Proms Online menu to look forward to.

So, in the future, should Siegfried ever have to utter those fateful words at a Proms concert, we'll be able to let you know just what Brünnhilde is thinking, and link you directly to a discussion on the music of love-at-first-sight …

www.bbc.co.uk/proms

ABOVE
Charles Hazlewood, conductor turned digitally interactive anchorman

TOP
How the stylish new in-vision programme notes appear

Proms on BBC Radio 3

Every Prom is broadcast live on BBC Radio 3 and many can be heard again on weekday afternoons at 2.00pm.

Proms Chamber Music concerts are all broadcast live and repeated the following Sunday at 1.00pm.

Proms Composer Portraits (see page 136) are broadcast later the same day.

Twenty Minutes programmes, broadcast in the intervals of evening Proms, include features and talks around this year's Proms theme and anniversaries.

In Tune (weekdays 5.00–7.30pm) features Proms-related interviews, performances and news.

Morning on 3 (daily 6.00–9.00am) will carry updates on the season.

Sunday Live (9.00am–12 noon) will also carry updates on the season and performances of the winning works in the BBC Proms/Guardian Young Composers' Competition.

BBC RADIO 3* 90-93 FM

Listen out too for the following special Proms-related programming:

Proms Preview Evening (Monday 14 July, 7.30–10.30pm) Musical highlights and the inside story on the coming season

Summer Selection (Saturdays, 9.00am–12 noon) Guest presenters – including Jenny Agutter, Deborah Bull, Simon Callow, Ian Hislop, Armando Iannucci and Vikram Seth – make their pick of forthcoming Proms alongside other choices.

Discovering Music (Sundays 5.00–5.45pm)
13 July   Tchaikovsky: Piano Concerto No. 1
20 July   Bartók: Concerto for Orchestra
27 July   Prokofiev: Piano Concerto No. 3
3 Aug   Berlioz: Harold in Italy

10 Aug   Sibelius: Violin Concerto
17 Aug   Ravel: Daphnis and Chloë
24 Aug   Brahms: Symphony No. 1
31 Aug   Holst: The Planets
7 Sept   Beethoven: Symphony No. 9

Proms Sunday Features (5.45–6.30pm)
20 July   **Baptising the Gods**
Exploring the vital relationship between modern Greeks and their ancient deities
27 July   **Ligeti**
A profile of one of the most original and enquiring figures in contemporary music
3 Aug   **Prokofiev**
The story of his love affair with America – from Ford cars to the movies
10 Aug   **The BBC Proms Lecture**
Peter Sellars: 'The Culture of Democracy' (see page 133)
17 Aug   **Berlioz**
The enduring enigma of a visionary musical genius and perpetual outsider

Times subject to change

BBC Proms Guide 2003

Published by BBC Proms Publications. Editorial Office: Room 4084, Broadcasting House, Portland Place, London W1A 1AA Distributed by BBC Worldwide, 80 Wood Lane, London W12 0TT

Editor Mark Pappenheim
Publications Manager Sarah Breeden
Editorial Manager David Threasher
Publications Officer Suzanne Esdell
Publications Assistant Hannah Rowley

Design Premm Design Ltd, London
Cover photograph (RAH) Simon Keats
Advertising Cabbell Publishing Ltd, London

Printed by Taylor Bloxham Ltd, Leicester

© BBC 2003
ISBN 0-563-48744-5

BBC Proms 2003

Director Nicholas Kenyon CBE, Controller, BBC Proms, Live Events and TV Classical Music

Personal Assistant Yvette Pusey
Artistic Administrator Rosemary Gent
Concerts Administrator Helen Burridge
Concerts Assistants Katy Blurton, Elisa Dunbar
Marketing Manager Kate Finch
Publicists Neil Evans, Victoria Bevan
Marketing and Audience Development Officer Doug Buist
Marketing & Publicity Assistant Jacqui Garbett
Finance Manager David Stott
Finance Assistant Ben Turner
Executive Producer, BBC Radio 3 Edward Blakeman

Proms on BBC Television

BBC1: Proms 2, 17 and 33 will be recorded for later showing; Prom 73 (Part 2) will be shown live.

BBC2: Proms 1, 29, 38, 45, 54 and 73 (Part 1) will be shown live. Prom 55 will be recorded for later showing.

BBC4: Proms 4, 6, 7, 9, 10, 12, 13, 14, 15, 17, 18, 19, 20 and 22 will be shown live.

Proms on BBC World Service

The BBC World Service broadcasts regular highlights from the season. Details on www.bbc.co.uk/worldservice

BBC Proms Online

www.bbc.co.uk/proms

The BBC Proms website is the place to come for all the news and information you need on the season, including full sets of programme notes for all 73 RAH concerts and handy 'quick guides' and 'behind the scenes' features. You can book tickets online, post your views and questions on our popular message board, and even compete for tickets by submitting

your own reviews. All 14 BBC4 concerts, plus the First and Last Nights, will be webcast, and several Proms will be available as 'Audio on Demand' for you to listen to for up to seven days after broadcast. You can also help choose the programme for 'The Nation's Favourite Prom' by voting online (see page 129).

All broadcast details were correct at the time of going to press. For current schedules, consult *Radio Times* or other listings publications, or visit the Proms website www.bbc.co.uk/proms

Index of Artists

Bold italic figures refer to Prom numbers
(PCM indicates Proms Chamber Music concerts: see pages 110–111).
* First appearance at a BBC Henry Wood Promenade Concert

Index of Works

Bold italic figures refer to Prom numbers (PCM indicates Proms Chamber Music concerts: see pages 110–111).
* First performance at a BBC Henry Wood Promenade Concert

A

John Adams (born 1947)
On the Transmigration of Souls* *13*
Kalevi Aho (born 1949)
Symphony No. 9* *40*

B

Johann Sebastian Bach (1685–1750)
Cantata No. 34, 'O ewiges Feuer' *16*
Cantata No. 170, 'Vergnügte Ruh, beliebte Seelenlust' *70*
Cantata No. 191, 'Gloria in excelsis Deo' *16*
Chaconne (from Partita, BWV 1004; arr. Busoni*) *PCM 2*
Concerto in C minor for oboe and violin, after BWV 1060 *5*
Samuel Barber (1910–81)
Medea's Meditation and Dance of Vengeance *41*
Béla Bartók (1881–1945)
Concerto for Orchestra *10*
Divertimento *32*
Music for Strings, Percussion and Celesta *55*
Piano Concerto No. 3 *13*
Arnold Bax (1883–1953)
November Woods *17*
Sally Beamish (born 1956)
Trumpet Concerto* *25*

Ludwig van Beethoven (1770–1827)
The Creatures of Prometheus – Overture *4*
Overture 'The Consecration of the House' *42*
Piano Concerto No. 1 in C major *27*
Piano Concerto No. 4 in G major *69*
Piano Concerto No. 5 in E flat major, 'Emperor' *59*
Piano Sonata in D minor, Op. 31 No. 2, 'The Tempest'* *PCM 2*
String Quartet in F minor, Op. 95, 'Serioso'* *PCM 6*
Symphony No. 2 in D major *53*
Symphony No. 3 in E flat major, 'Eroica' *44*
Symphony No. 5 in C minor *9*
Symphony No. 6 in F major, 'Pastoral' *18*
Symphony No. 7 in A major *33*
Symphony No. 9 in D minor, 'Choral' *72*
Alban Berg (1885–1935)
Seven Early Songs *50*
Lennox Berkeley (1903–89)
Magnificat, Op. 71 *61*
Michael Berkeley (born 1948)
Secret Garden* *60*
Hector Berlioz (1803–69)
Benvenuto Cellini *39*
The Childhood of Christ *14*
The Damnation of Faust – excerpts *PCM 8*
The Damnation of Faust – Hungarian March *2*
Harold in Italy *29*
La mort de Cléopâtre *42*
La mort d'Orphée – Monologue and Larghetto* *PCM 8*
Les nuits d'été *12*
Overture 'Roman Carnival' *73*
Romeo and Juliet – excerpts *PCM 8*
Symphonie fantastique *43*
The Trojans – Part 1 'The Capture of Troy' *47*
The Trojans – Part 2 'The Trojans at Carthage' *48*

Sir Harrison Birtwistle (born 1934)
Nenia: The Death of Orpheus *36*
The Shadow of Night* *72*
Georges Bizet (1838–75)
Carmen – 'L'amour est un oiseau rebelle' (Habanera) *73*
Alexander Borodin (1833–87)
Prince Igor – Polovtsian Dances *73*
Johannes Brahms (1833–97)
A German Requiem *37*
Horn Trio* *PCM 3*
Piano Concerto No. 1 in D minor *4*
Symphony No. 1 in C minor *50*
Symphony No. 2 in D major *59*
Symphony No. 4 in E minor *27*
Variations on the St Anthony Chorale *56*
Violin Concerto in D major *52*
Frank Bridge (1879–1941)
Oration – Concerto elegiaco for cello and orchestra* *60*
Benjamin Britten (1913–76)
Folk Song arrangements *2*
Six Metamorphoses after Ovid *PCM 1*
Phaedra *65*
Young Apollo* *51*
The Young Person's Guide to the Orchestra *17*
Anton Bruckner (1824–96)
Motets: 'Christus factus est'; 'Virga Jesse floruit'; 'Ave Maria' *36*
Symphony No. 5 in B flat major *57*
Antoine Busnoys (c1430–92)
Fortuna desperata* *62*
William Byrd (1543–1623)
In nomine II* *62*
Quomodo cantabimus* *PCM 5*

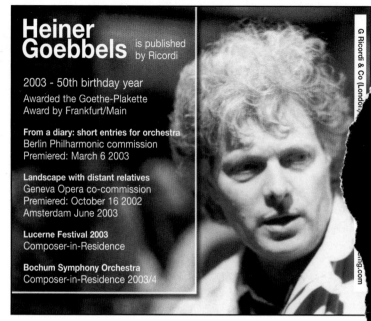